BETTER WAY BOOKS

DIET

COOKBOOK

Contents

Back to the Kitchen 4
Becoming a low-calorie cook is the best way to fight the most harmful food additive: calories.

Suit Your Taste 7
How to custom design your own diet to meet your nutritional needs and suit your tastes.

Calorie Coping 13
Cooking, shopping and eating hints can slash the calorie content of favorite recipes.

Delicious Breakfasts 18
Satisfying breakfasts to keep you away from junk foods include Hotcakes, Savory Sausage and more.

Superb Salads and Dressings 23
Recipes for superb coleslaws, other garden-fresh delights and low-cal dressings.

The Best Vegetable Dishes 29
Top-of-the-crop vegetable recipes from artichoke hearts to zucchini.

Skinny Potatoes, Pasta and Rice 41
Low-calorie versions of such dieter's downfalls as Stuffed Potatoes, Shell Salad and Spaghetti and Meatballs.

Meat Facts and Fallacies 48
Here are the best low-calorie cooking methods for bringing out the flavor in beef. Recipes range from Pot Roast Olé to Smothered Baked Steak.

Luscious Veal 59
Calorie-bargain recipes for Veal Picatta and Low-Fat Veal Parmigiana.

Printed in Canada

Versatile Lamb   **64**
Succulent recipes include Chinese Sweet 'n' Sour
Lamb, Lamb and Artichokes en Brochette and others.

Slim Pork and Ham   **69**
Decalorized recipes include Pork Steak Viennese,
Pinapple-Ham Stir Fry and other surprisingly low-
calorie dishes.

Ground Meat Favorites   **74**
Lean and tasty ways with hamburger and other ground
meats include Succulent Burgers, Turkey Chili, and
more.

Chicken and Turkey   **79**
Low-calorie ways to cook savory dishes such as
Chicken Mediterranean and Oven-Fried Chicken.

Seafood Supreme   **91**
Tips for buying and cooking fish, plus delicious recipes
like Turkish Baked Sea Steaks and Shrimp Bisque.

Unforbidden Sweets   **101**
Luscious no-sugar recipes include pies, cream puffs,
dessert crepes and other goodies.

Index   **127**

ISBN 0-88176-302-0

Cover Design: Jeff Hapner

Back to the Kitchen

The first step in losing weight is to get back into the kitchen. Declare your independence from gooey frozen pastries and TV dinners. Take charge of what goes onto your plate, into your mouth, and onto your hips. Learn to cook all over again, the low-calorie way.

Most lose-weight prescriptions take just the opposite approach, putting a psychological padlock on the kitchen door by telling the reader to forget about food. How can anybody forget about food? Particularly when we are constantly surrounded by food cues. No-work, no-nutrition, high-calorie snacks scream at us constantly from the TV screen, magazine pages, and supermarket ads. Nobody — least of all a person with a weight problem — can remain immune without alternative satisfactions. However, if you can duplicate the taste and texture of the foods you love — without the unneeded extra calories — you can turn a deaf ear!

Become a low-calorie cook. It needn't be time-consuming. With the variety of foods available today — including many convenience foods that are calorie bargains — low-cal cooking is easier than ever. Modern appliances, a well-equipped kitchen, a roomy refrigerator-freezer, and one-stop supermarkets, simplify the job. So do the recipes in this book. Short-cutting preparation time has been considered along with short-cutting calories.

Why Are You Overweight?

You are overweight because you take in more calories than you use up! But so do millions of other Americans, nearly half the population. The fact that so many others are in the same boat is small comfort. The health costs of carrying around your excess burden are just as high no matter how many others share your plight.

The fact that so many people fall beyond the American ideal of slenderness in no way lessens the discrimination overweights are subjected to. Excess pounds cost you money — in terms of lost income and lost opportunity. It has been well documented that fat job applicants lose out to less-qualified slim competitors. Fat executives are passed over for promotion. Fat salesmen, waitresses, and taxi drivers lose commissions and tips, often from fat customers. Even fat people don't like fat people!

In no other society has food been so easily attainable for so little physical effort. Despite inflation and soaring prices, despite occasional shortages, Americans still enjoy the "benefits" of a too bountiful breadbasket — with very little sweat of the brow in payment. You may hate your job, but sitting down at a desk all day doesn't qualify as work, not in the physical sense.

It is ironic that a society that makes the accumulation of fat so easy — almost unavoidable — should profess such an intolerance for obesity. The social pressures to avoid overweight are enormous, but they serve a purpose. Our skinny actresses, flat-gutted athletes, society-page darlings, and other beautiful people do serve a function after all. The standard they set for slimness has made fat unfashionable. And in the long run, vanity is what keeps most of us from eating ourselves into our graves.

Our Most Harmful Food Additive: Calories

Today, family life is increasingly fragmentized, with each individual snacking on the run. Long, late commuter hours between job and home (for Mom as well as

Dad), a busy schedule of after-school activities, summers spent at camp, and semesters spent away at college all mean that more Americans of every age are eating outside the home. Even home-cooked meals are less likely to be cooked than thawed and served. The result is that Americans have less control than ever before over what goes into the food they eat.

A good Italian cook would make her homemade ravioli with lots of meat and simmer it with fresh tomatoes. But meat and vegetables are expensive, so a food processing firm that packages frozen ravioli is likely to stuff it with yet more starch, flavor it with a little meat, and freeze it in a tomato-shy sauce that's thickened with syrups and fillers. The second generation Italian-American wife who serves it to her family concedes wistfully that it's not quite like Mama used to make. She's probably not aware that the store-bought product is also more fattening, less nourishing, and less filling because the ravioli is short on appetite-appeasing protein while overly generous with quick-burning carbohydrates. A few hours after their ravioli meal, her family is foraging in the refrigerator for something else to fill their now-empty stomachs. More high-cal snacks fill the void.

This example is multiplied a thousandfold. Just think of all the breaded fish sticks, frozen fried chicken, boiling-bag vegetables, toaster pastries, sugar-coated cereals, stir-and-serve puddings, spray-on cheese spreads, and can-opener soups and sauces Americans haul home by the tons from supermarkets — in addition to obvious junk foods like candy, soft drinks, chips, dips, and nibbles.

You might think that the American food industry has purposely set out to make us fat. Just when the technological revolution has entrapped an ever-widening circle of Americans of all ages and both sexes into sit-down jobs (or more years of sit-down schooling), just when our national calorie needs are at their lowest, food manufacturers seem to respond with a bulging cornucopia of nutritionally-neutered junk food, food that requires us to eat more and more calories for less and less nutrition.

Suit Your Taste

Everybody knows that eating lots of food and accumulating extra pounds is no guarantee of adequate nutrition. Many Americans are overfed but undernourished because their tastes run to empty-caloried junk. When a person with a taste for fattening foods attempts to lose weight by simply cutting down, his or her chances of nutritional deficiency are multiplied. So before you become a bookkeeper of calories, it's important to understand that all calories are not alike, and that your calories must come from a variety of food sources for you to remain healthy.

Spending calories is like managing money. The shrewd manager knows that all bills must be paid before the leftovers can be spent on frills. Some people can live comfortably on little, while others spend a great deal and still run into trouble. The undernourished overweight is like a person who buys a car he or she cannot afford, while neglecting to pay the mortgage.

The person who wants to lose weight is in the same situation as somebody who has to live on a reduced income for awhile. Intelligent, imaginative people will find creative ways to do it in reasonable comfort, knowing that the time isn't far off when they can loosen up a little and indulge in a few more luxuries. But the smart dieter knows that a time when basic nutritional needs can be ignored will *never* come.

Protein, Fat, Carbohydrate . . . and Calories

Protein, fat, and carbohydrate are the basic food elements. A balanced diet includes all three. It is nearly impossible to emphasize or eliminate one without causing an unwanted imbalance in another. Therefore, when dieting, it is important to keep each of these elements in a healthy balance without simply cutting out one whole food type.

That's the idea behind the nutritional figures provided with each of the recipes in this book. Once you have computed your daily requirement of calories (see Computing Your Calorie Needs), the carbohydrate, protein, and fat figures given with each recipe will help you determine what percentages of your daily intake are being made up of these vital food elements.

Protein is mainly animal food — meat, poultry, fish, and eggs. But none is pure protein. Each also contains fat, and the more fat, the less protein. Protein is also found in dairy products like milk and cheese, and, along with fat and carbohydrate, in vegetables like beans and nuts. Protein is vital to life because the body needs it to build and repair itself. Protein is also valuable to dieters because it is slowly digested and helps sustain a feeling of fullness.

Approximately 25 percent of the food you eat should be protein; the minimum is 14 percent. But there is no benefit in having more protein than you need because the excess is stored by the body as fat. Too much protein has been linked with calcium deficiency and kidney disorders.

Fat can be either animal (meat fat or butter, for example) or vegetable (margarine, salad oil, or the fat found in nuts). Calorically, it does not matter where it comes from because both animal and vegetable fat have the same calorie count — double the calories of either protein or carbohydrate. Even for very determined dieters, it would be both difficult and undesirable to eliminate fat from the diet altogether because a small amount is needed to help the body absorb nutrients properly. But no more than 30 to 35 percent of the total calories you consume each day should be in the form of fat.

The last columns in the nutritional figures after the recipes in this book tell how much of the fat is saturated fat and how much cholesterol there is. The American Heart Association tells us to keep saturated fats to a minimum because they contain the cholesterol that is believed to be linked with heart disease. Less than 10 percent of your daily total fat intake should be in the form of saturated fats. And the average daily intake of cholesterol should be no more than 300 milligrams.

Carbohydrate is found in the sugars and starches we love so much. A diet plan that attempts to eliminate carbohydrate is a poor idea because fruits and vegetables, which are relatively high in carbohydrate, are the main sources of vital vitamins and minerals, as well as appetite-appeasing fiber.

Approximately 43 percent of a balanced diet should be carbohydrate. A diet that's low in carbohydrate is likely to be too high in fat and protein with possibly serious consequences. To maintain health, at least 60 grams of carbohydrate must be present in any daily diet. What should be avoided in the carbohydrate category are refined sugars and overprocessed starches that have been stripped of everything worthwhile, leaving little but calories.

And calories? A calorie is actually a measure of heat — fuel to power our bodies. If we consume more fuel than we can use up, the excess is stored as unsightly bulges. Calories exist in all foods, otherwise they would not be food. There are roughly four calories in every gram of protein or carbohydrate, and about nine calories in every gram of fat. To lose weight, we need to eat a variety of foods that are high in nutritional value but low in fuel value (calories) so that the body will be forced to use up its excess.

Fiber

Until recently, food fiber was the "forgotten nutrient" because it's not a nutrient at all. Fiber is the non-caloric, non-nutritious, nondigestible part of plant foods — the roughage or bulk in fruits, vegetables, nuts, seeds and whole-grain cereal foods. Since it's not digested but eliminated, it generally doesn't appear on nutrition charts and its importance has been ignored. But current research suggests that our reliance on over-refined processed foods from which much of the fiber has been removed may be related to many diseases, everything from cancer to constipation, from appendicitis to overweight!

Most foods high in fiber are naturally low in calories. They are important to dieters because their bulkiness fills the stomach and minimizes the desire or ability to overeat. Fiber is important to everyone because it speeds food through the system and minimizes constipation. Constipation has been related to diverticulosis, hemorrhoids, varicose veins and colon cancer. Vegetable fiber, particularly the pectin in fresh fruits, has been shown to aid in the elimination of excess fats and cholesterol from the system. So eating more foods that are naturally high in fiber is a good idea for most people, but especially for dieters. On the other hand, the extremes of fiber consumption suggested in some books on the topic, like all extremes, should be avoided.

Dietary Goals

Early in 1977, the U.S. Senate Select Committee on Nutrition issued a significant report: "Dietary Goals for the United States." This report urged sweeping changes in America's eating patterns. The Senate panel noted that Americans have been eating far too much sugar and fatty food, and not enough fruits, vegetables, grains, and other complex carbohydrates. The Senate said that current eating habits may be "as profoundly damaging to the nation's health as the widespread contagious diseases of the early part of the century." Here are those dietary goals:

- Increase carbohydrate consumption to account for 55 to 60 percent of calorie intake.
- Reduce overall fat consumption from approximately 40 to 30 percent of calorie intake.
- Reduce saturated fat consumption to account for about 10 percent of total calorie intake; and balance with polyunsaturated and monounsaturated fats, which should each account for about 10 percent of calorie intake.
- Reduce cholesterol consumption to about 300 milligrams a day.
- Reduce sugar consumption by almost 40 percent.
- Reduce salt consumption by about 50 to 85 percent.

To achieve these goals, the committee suggests the following changes in food selection and preparation:

- Increase consumption of fruits and vegetables and whole grains.
- Decrease consumption of meat and increase consumption of poultry and fish.
- Decrease consumption of foods high in fat, and partially substitute polyunsaturated fat for saturated fat.
- Substitute nonfat milk for whole milk.
- Decrease consumption of butterfat, eggs, and other high-cholesterol sources.
- Decrease consumption of sugar and foods with high sugar content.
- Decrease consumption of salt and foods with high salt content.

All of the recipes in this book reflect the Senate committee's goals and suggestions. The ingredients called for are in all cases the low-fat, low-calorie, unsweetened versions of or substitutions for common cooking ingredients. Cholesterol is also reduced not only by the choice of ingredients but also by special methods of preparation described in the recipes and chapter introductions. Not one recipe calls for sugar or even sugar substitute; naturally sweet fruits and fruit juices provide the desirable sweetness in sauces, desserts, beverages, and other foods. At the end of each recipe, there is also an analysis of the calories, carbohydrate, protein, total fat, saturated fat and cholesterol for the total yield of the recipe and for each serving.

Eating to get thin or stay thin really amounts to healthy eating. So even if you are the only one at your house who is trying to lose weight, your whole family will benefit from the dishes made with the ingredients and methods described in this book.

Computing Your Calorie Needs

If you are an extremely inactive person who eats 3000 calories a day, your weight will eventually stabilize somewhere over the 200 mark. On the other hand, a young active person forced to live on 1500 calories might eventually become a 98-pound weakling. The right combination for you is somewhere between those two extremes.

Most diets expect the lifelong overeater to become an undereater overnight. It is unrealistic to believe that a 3000-calorie-a-day person can summon up the willpower to eat like a 98-pound weakling — unrealistic and unnecessary. If those same overweights simply began eating like the normalweights they want to be, their weight would eventually stabilize at the desired point on the scale. So the first step on your program is determining your proper weight and then computing the calorie intake that can eventually bring you there.

Calorie Coping

By providing yourself with a few special diet utensils and by using some easy cooking, shopping and eating hints, you can slash the calorie content of your favorite foods and daily intake, and lose weight in a painless and delicious way.

Equipment

• Equip yourself with nonstick pots and pans for cooking, baking and frying without fat. Follow the manufacturer's directions for care. Inexpensive utensils can do the job if you keep them well scrubbed. If a skillet loses its ability to cook without added fat, throw it out. You cannot afford to keep it!

• A pressure cooker is a handy gadget for cooks on the go because it cuts cooking time by one-third. The leanest, least fattening, less-expensive cuts of meat profit from pressure cookery. If you buy a new one, choose a model with a nonstick interior.

• A blender makes short work of many kitchen tasks. Dieters can turn a blender into a milkshake maker by combining skim milk powder, ice cubes, water and flavoring. A handful of fresh berries or other fruit can be added for a garden-fresh flavor.

Cooking hints

• Use spray-on vegetable coating for no-fat frying. When used in conjunction with nonstick utensils, the spray eliminates the need for any added fat at all. The base of these products is lecithin, a natural food component much loved by health food fans.

- When making stews and other combination dishes, prepare them a day ahead and store them in the refrigerator — all day or overnight — until serving time. The flavors blend better and all the fat rises to the surface where you can easily lift it off.
- Fat can be removed from the surface of stock, soup, or gravy with a bulb-type baster or by chilling until the fat rises and can be lifted off.
- Keep your crisper well stocked with shredded lettuce, chopped onion and other greenery so that serving a salad at every meal is a snap.
- Keep your refrigerator's fruit compartment well supplied with whatever fresh treats are in season. Fruit makes the perfect dessert. Freeze fruits in season for sugar-free treats during the winter.
- If time is at a premium (and when isn't it?), cook in double or triple quantities. Then package the leftovers into homemade low-calorie frozen dinners. Inexpensive aluminum pie pans can serve this purpose.
- Large roasts, casseroles and other dishes meant for several meals should be packaged away in the freezer right after dinner. Don't keep leftovers around.
- Package meats and other foods for the freezer in serving-size quantities. Four to six ounces of boneless raw meat per person is about right. If you defrost and cook only what you need, you avoid waste.

Calorie-Coping in the Supermarket

- Be a calorie-comparison shopper. Check the nutritional label panel of competing products and choose the one with the lower calorie count. Smart label-readers can save calories the same way a cost-wise shopper saves money.
- Always look for the lowest fat content in dairy products. Cottage cheese that is labeled 99 percent fat-free is only 160 to 180 calories a cup. Regular creamed cottage cheese is 240 to 260.
- Do not pay a premium price for fattening meat. Prime meat, the most expensive, has a higher ratio of

fat and calories and less protein than less costly grades.

- In choosing meat, always look for the leanest cuts. Have the butcher trim away all fat, or do it yourself. Trimmable exterior fat is less of a problem than fatty marbling all through the meat.

- Play the substitution game. Look for diet-right versions of fattening products. Experiment with them in recipes.

- Low-calorie cream cheese and part-skim Neufchatel cheese have the same flavor as fattening cream cheese, and perform the same way in recipes.

- Evaporated skim milk can take the place of cream in most sauces, casseroles, souffles, and desserts. It can even be whipped!

- Yogurt or buttermilk can take the place of sour cream in many recipes. Or look for low-fat, nondairy sour cream dressings that can serve the same function. But check the calorie count. Some nondairy dressings contain just as much fat (vegetable instead of animal) as real sour cream.

- Diet margarine has half the calories of regular margarine or butter because it is half water. Unfortunately it cannot replace ordinary margarine in regular recipes. However, many recipes in this book are adjusted to use this low-in-calories spread.

- Low-fat diet dressings and mayonnaise substitute can help keep salads slimming.

- Do not be put off by the word *imitation* on certain low-calorie, low-sugar, or low-fat products. The word doesn't mean that the product is made up of chemicals, but only that the lower sugar or fat content keeps the product from conforming to standard recipes. Often the imitations are more nutritious than the real thing.

- Beware the dietetic product that does not list its calorie count! It may not be diet-wise at all, but simply salt-free. For example, some dietetic candies made for diabetics have just as many calories as regular candy.

- Bottled flavorings and extracts from the supermarket spice shelf are calorie bargains. Some to look for include butter flavoring, rum, brandy, banana, and chocolate. Most spices and seasonings add so few calories to a dish that they do not need to be counted.

- Never go shopping when you are hungry. And leave the kids at home.

Calorie-Coping in the Dining Room

One of the most successful new approaches to weight control is behavior modification. This technique helps overweight people cut calories by forcing them to focus on unconscious eating habits. You can put these methods to work in the dining room by following a few simple rules:

- Never eat standing up. By following this rule, you preclude all nibbling, tasting, testing, and snacking.

- Always eat in the same place, the dining room, for example. Even if you are determined to eat that leftover half-donut, set yourself a place at the dining table, then sit down and eat it. By the time everything is set, you may have changed your mind.

- Always set your place properly. Use a place mat, napkin, water glass, the whole bit. You'll enjoy your meal more in a pleasant setting, and the act of setting a place makes each meal a ceremony.

- Never eat while reading or watching TV. Do not dilute the enjoyment of food by concentrating your attention on something else. Paperwork, crossword puzzles, business negotiations, and family arguments shouldn't cut into your eating pleasure either.

- Never prepare or put out more food than you need, lest you personally clean up the leftovers yourself. Leave the second helpings in the kitchen so you'll have to make a special trip to get them.

- Always compute the number of servings in any dish you make — main course, side dish, or dessert — and apportion it accordingly. If a dish serves six, make it a point to serve yourself one-sixth of the total, and not a tablespoon more.

- Set out at one time everything you plan to eat at a meal, from soup to dessert. With the finale in full view, you'll be less likely to overeat at the main event.

• Equip yourself with smaller plates. Choose a restaurant-style design, with wide rims. A brimming luncheon-size plate is more eye-satisfying than a big expanse of china with lots of white space around modest servings of food. The same strategy applies to wine glasses and dessert dishes.

• Use the other tactic with salads and vegetable dishes. Serve your salad in big soup-size bowls to encourage yourself to fill up on nonfattening fare.

• Do not concentrate on easy-to-eat foods. Foods that take longer to consume are more satisfying than boneless, bite-size swallows. Corn on the cob seems like more than the same amount of cut corn. Lobster in the shell will keep you busy longer than a boneless steak.

• Eat slowly, savor each bite.

. . . and Away from It!

• Once you are finished eating, leave the table. Do not keep others company.

• Do not clean up when you clean the table. If you cannot resist munching on the leftovers, put a piece of gum in your mouth before you start. Or better yet, turn the clean-up job over to somebody else.

• Keep busy. Get out of the house during those crisis hours when you're most inclined to succumb to a peanut butter frenzy. Go window shopping for the new clothes you'll buy when you're slim.

• Take up a hobby, preferably something that keeps your hands busy. It's hard to eat potato chips and refinish furniture at the same time. A good idea is to take up sewing — you'll need seamstress skills to create the new wardrobe in your thin future.

• Make a list of everything you hate about being fat, and post it prominently on the refrigerator. Or take the positive approach and list all the things you'd do if you were trim.

Delicious Breakfasts

If skipping breakfast is your idea of saving calories, think again. Would-be skinnies who try to subsist without breakfast generally wind up giving into coffee-and-junk breaks at midmorning, or overeating at lunch, or both. The result is more calories consumed than would have been in a decent morning meal.

Breakfast needn't be heavy or elaborate. In fact, if you're dieting, it should be light. But lightness in calories does not mean shortchanging nutrition. Ideally, a dieter's breakfast should include:

• Fresh fruit for vitamins and bulk. Unsugared canned or frozen fruit can be used. High-in-vitamin-C choices like grapefruit, sliced strawberries, or melon are ideal.

• Grain, which can be either bread or cereal.

• Protein food. Meat or eggs or egg substitutes are the usual choices. High-protein cereals topped with protein-rich skim milk can also meet your morning protein requirement.

- Milk — preferably nonfat or low-fat, which can be a beverage by itself, poured on cereal or fruit, or used in coffee or tea.

Good Breakfast Combinations

- High-protein cereal with skim milk and sliced berries.
- Grapefruit half, toasted protein bread with low-calorie cream cheese.
- Melon wedge, cottage-cheese-filled omelet, and black coffee. Toast saved for a 10 o'clock snack.
- Pancakes made with high-protein pancake mix, topped with sliced strawberries or crushed pineapple. Add a glass of skim milk.

If you're a confirmed coffee-breaker, there's no harm in saving part of your breakfast menu for a midmorning snack. However, postponing all food until 10 or 11 o'clock is a poor idea since it is likely that more than half a day has passed since your body took in any nourishment.

Bad Breakfast Bets

At the other extreme from breakfast-skippers are those who unwittingly load up on calories without redeeming nutritional value. Many traditional breakfast foods are exceedingly rich in sugar, starch, or fat.

- **Sugar-coated cereals.** Most presweetened cereals contain more sugar than anything else. When choosing cereal, pick a high-protein variety.
- **Bacon** is more than half fat, even after it has been broiled or fried and well drained. Choose lean Canadian bacon instead, only 45 calories an ounce instead of 200.
- **Sausage** is generally 50 percent fat. Instead of buying packaged sausage, make your own home-seasoned patties from lean ground pork.
- **Pastries** are simply empty-caloried concoctions of starch, sugar, and fat. Their low protein means you'll be hungry by midmorning.

Recipes

Blueberry Cornmeal Muffins

2/3 cup diet margarine
2 eggs
1¼ cups cornmeal
¾ cup flour
2½ tsp. double-acting
    baking powder
¾ tsp. salt
¾ cup skimmed milk

½ cup fresh
    blueberries or
    unsweetened
    frozen
    blueberries,
    thawed and
    drained

Beat the diet margarine and eggs in a medium bowl. Stir in the cornmeal. Sift the flour and remeasure to ¾ cup. Sift again with the baking powder and salt. Stir ⅓ of this mixture into the cornmeal mixture. Then stir in ½ of the milk. Repeat this process. Add the remaining ⅓ of flour mixture. Gently fold in the blueberries. Place a scant ¼ cup of batter in each cup of a muffin tin that has been sprayed with vegetable coating. Bake the muffins in a preheated 350° oven for 20 to 25 minutes until golden brown.   *Makes 15 servings*

	Calories	Carbo-hydrate (gm)	Protein (gm)	Total Fat (gm)	Saturated Fat (gm)	Choles-terol (mg)
Total	1194.3	204.8	42.9	23.6	6.0	507.8
Per Serving	79.6	13.7	2.9	1.6	0.4	33.9

gm = grams; mg = milligrams. Nutritional figures are approximate. Figures are based on findings of U.S. Department of Agriculture.

High-Protein Waffles

1 whole egg or 2 egg
whites
1 tsp. vanilla

½ cup soy-enriched
pancake mix
½ cup skim milk

Stir the egg, vanilla and pancake mix together and add just enough milk to make a pourable batter. Spray the surface of your nonstick waffle maker with vegetable coating until all surfaces are wet and shiny. Turn on the heat. When a drop of water bounces and sizzles, pour on the batter and close the waffle maker. Don't attempt to open until the waffles stop steaming or the indicator light goes off. When the waffles are done, loosen gently with a fork or knife, being careful not to mar the nonstick surface.

Makes 4 sections (2 servings)

	Calories	Carbo-hydrate (gm)	Protein (gm)	Total Fat (gm)	Saturated Fat (gm)	Choles-terol (mg)
Total	335.0	48.0	20.5	34.0	2.0	254.5
Per Serving	167.5	24.0	10.3	17.0	1.0	127.3

Hotcakes

1 cup flour
1 tsp. baking powder
¼ tsp. salt

1 cup skim milk
1 egg, slightly
beaten

Sift the flour and remeasure to 1 cup. Sift again with the baking powder and salt. In a mixing bowl, combine the milk with the beaten egg; then add the dry ingredients. Blend the mixture only until the larger lumps disappear. Spray a nonstick skillet with vegetable coating for no-fat frying and preheat the skillet over medium-low heat for 2 to 3 minutes or until a drop of water sizzles on the surface. With a tablespoon, drop the batter to make 4-inch hotcakes in the hot pan, and cook about 1 minute per side. Serve immediately.

Makes 12 hotcakes (6 servings)

	Calories	Carbo-hydrate (gm)	Protein (gm)	Total Fat (gm)	Saturated Fat (gm)	Choles-terol (mg)
Total	627.1	107.5	28.0	7.0	2.0	257.0
Per Serving	104.5	17.9	4.7	1.2	0.3	42.8

Savory Sausage

4 lb. lean pork
    shoulder, trimmed
    of all fat and
    ground twice
1 tbsp. onion salt
1 finely chopped garlic
    clove
1 tbsp. sage

1 tsp. ground cloves
1 tsp. mace
2 tsp. pepper
1 tbsp. minced
    parsley
1/4 tsp. ground
    allspice

Combine the ground pork with the other ingredients and mix well. Shape the meat into 3-oz. patties. (This will make 20 patties.) The patties may be broiled 3 to 4 inches from heat source or pan-fried in a nonstick skillet. Cook until they are no longer pink inside.

Makes 20 servings

Note: The raw patties may be frozen for later cooking.

	Calories	Carbo-hydrate (gm)	Protein (gm)	Total Fat (gm)	Saturated Fat (gm)	Choles-terol (mg)
Total	4666.5	0.0	533.2	266.6	80.0	1599.6
Per Serving	233.3	0.0	26.7	13.3	4.0	80.0

Country Sausage

2 tbsp. sage
1 tbsp. salt
1 tsp. pepper
1 tsp. ground cloves

1/2 tsp. ground
    nutmeg
4 lb. lean fresh pork,
    trimmed of all fat
    and ground

Add the seasonings to the meat and mix until well blended. Shape the meat into 3-oz. patties. Broil 3 to 4 inches from the heat source or pan-fry in a nonstick skillet until they are no longer pink inside.

Makes 20 servings

Note: The raw patties may be frozen for later cooking.

	Calories	Carbo-hydrate (gm)	Protein (gm)	Total Fat (gm)	Saturated Fat (gm)	Choles-terol (mg)
Total	4666.5	0.0	533.2	266.6	80.0	1599.6
Per Serving	233.3	0.0	26.7	13.3	4.0	80.0

Superb Salads and Dressings

Salads, as everybody knows, are slimming. Or are they? Although the business end of a salad is slim, the toppings and trimmings are often a weight-inflating wipeout. A whole bowlful of shredded lettuce weighs in at less than 100 calories, but 2 tablespoons of bottled French dressing add 120 calories or more. Mayonnaise is almost as fattening as butter, close to 1600 calories a cupful.

Luckily for waistline-watchers, salad dressing makers have come to the rescue with a variety of slimmed-down toppings with only a fraction of the usual fat and calories. Low-cal versions of nearly every favorite are available: French, Italian, Russian, bleu cheese, Caesar, coleslaw, mayonnaise. Name it and you'll find it somewhere.

The savings are not to be sneered at. Consider, for example, the caloric comparison of a tuna salad made with a 7-ounce can of water-packed tuna and 5 tablespoons diet mayonnaise: total, 320 calories. The same tuna salad made with oil-packed tuna and regular mayonnaise would add up to a whopping 1077 calories.

Because salads are chock full of vitamins and appetite-appeasing fiber, they should be a daily part of every dieter's slim-down plan. Here's a variety of salad ideas, proof that salads can be delicious and exciting. For do-it-yourself dressing makers, we also have included a number of decalorized variations of fattening favorites — all designed to take salad dressings off the forbidden list.

Recipes

Bleu Pear Salad

1 fresh pear, cored and
    diced
1 cup diced celery

½ cup low-calorie
    bleu cheese
    dressing

Combine all of the ingredients and serve on lettuce.

Makes 4 servings

	Calories	Carbo-hydrate (gm)	Protein (gm)	Total Fat (gm)	Saturated Fat (gm)	Choles-terol (mg)
Total	203.0	35.8	4.2	7.4	0.0	0.0
Per Serving	50.8	9.0	1.1	1.9	0.0	0.0

Tangy Apple Coleslaw

¼ tsp. celery seeds
1 tsp. salt
¼ cup evaporated
    skim milk
¼ cup diet
    mayonnaise
2 tbsp. cider vinegar

1 tsp. dry mustard
1 large red apple, diced
6 lightly packed cups
    shredded green
    cabbage (about a
    2¼ lb. head)

Whisk together all of the ingredients, except the apple
and cabbage, in a medium mixing bowl. Then mix in
the apple and cabbage. Cover the coleslaw and chill it
until ready to serve.

Makes 6 servings

	Calories	Carbo-hydrate (gm)	Protein (gm)	Total Fat (gm)	Saturated Fat (gm)	Choles-terol (mg)
Total	358.2	60.0	10.5	13.0	2.7	51.5
Per Serving	59.7	10.0	1.8	2.2	0.5	8.6

Colorful Coleslaw

5 cups finely shredded
green cabbage
1 cup shredded raw
carrot
1 red apple, peeled,
cored, and diced

¼ cup chopped green
pepper
½ cup evaporated
skim milk
¼ tsp. salt
⅛ tsp. pepper
¼ cup cider vinegar

Combine the cabbage, carrot, apple, and green pepper. Blend evaporated skim milk, salt, and pepper together in a small bowl. Gradually stir in the vinegar. Pour the dressing over the vegetables, and toss lightly to blend. Cover the coleslaw and chill it until you are ready to serve.   *Makes 6 servings*

	Calories	Carbo-hydrate (gm)	Protein (gm)	Total Fat (gm)	Saturated Fat (gm)	Choles-terol (mg)
Total	390.3	70.0	16.3	10.0	5.5	39.0
Per Serving	65.1	11.7	2.7	1.7	0.9	6.5

Coleslaw

4 cups shredded
cabbage
½ small onion, minced

4 tbsp. diet
mayonnaise
4 tbsp. plain low-fat
yogurt

Combine all ingredients and chill before serving.
Makes 4 servings

	Calories	Carbo-hydrate (gm)	Protein (gm)	Total Fat (gm)	Saturated Fat (gm)	Choles-terol (mg)
Total	211.3	32.3	7.0	9.0	0.5	37.0
Per Serving	52.8	8.1	1.8	2.3	0.1	9.3

gm = grams; mg = milligrams. Nutritional figures are approximate. Figures are based on findings of U.S. Department of Agriculture.

Salade Vinaigrette

3 tbsp. vinegar
1 tbsp. corn or safflower
oil
1/2 tsp. salt
1/4 tsp. ground black
pepper
1/4 tsp. basil

1 tsp. instant minced
onion
1 medium cucumber,
peeled and
sliced
3 large tomatoes,
sliced and
chilled

Combine the vinegar, oil, salt, pepper, basil, and onion in a jar or shaker. Shake the mixture well and pour it over the cucumber slices. Cover this mixture and chill it for 1 hour. Before serving, pour the cucumber mixture over the sliced tomatoes and mix gently.

Makes 8 servings

	Calories	Carbo-hydrate (gm)	Protein (gm)	Total Fat (gm)	Saturated Fat (gm)	Choles-terol (mg)
Total	401.2	64.7	13.1	14.0	1.0	0.0
Per Serving	50.2	8.1	1.6	1.8	0.1	0.0

Fresh Mushroom Medley

1 lb. fresh mushrooms,
sliced
1 cup diced celery
1 cup diced green
pepper
2 tbsp. finely chopped
onion

1 tbsp. olive oil
1 tbsp. wine vinegar
2 tsp. salt
1/8 tsp. ground black
pepper
2 tbsp. lemon juice

Place the sliced mushrooms, celery, green pepper, and onion in a salad bowl. Mix the remaining ingredients in another bowl. Then pour this mixture over the vegetables and toss gently. *Makes 6 servings*

	Calories	Carbo-hydrate (gm)	Protein (gm)	Total Fat (gm)	Saturated Fat (gm)	Choles-terol (mg)
Total	509.0	69.9	36.4	19.0	2.0	0.0
Per Serving	84.8	11.7	6.1	3.2	0.3	0.0

Garden Salad

1½ cups 99% fat-free
    cottage cheese
5 tbsp. diet mayonnaise
1½ tsp. salt
1 cup shredded carrot
2 cups thinly sliced
    celery

1 cup diced
    cucumber,
    unpeeled
½ cup chopped
    green or red
    pepper
¼ cup sliced
    radishes
¼ cup chopped
    onion

Combine the ingredients and chill before serving.

Makes 8 servings

	Calories	Carbo-hydrate (gm)	Protein (gm)	Total Fat (gm)	Saturated Fat (gm)	Cholesterol (mg)
Total	482.3	46.1	48.7	13.0	1.8	69.1
Per Serving	60.3	5.8	6.1	1.6	0.2	8.6

Lean Bean Salad

16-oz. can sliced green
    beans, drained
16-oz. can French-style
    sliced yellow
    beans, drained
¼ cup onion flakes
1 cup diced celery

½ envelope French
    salad dressing
    mix
1 cup buttermilk
2 tbsp. finely
    chopped
    pimiento
½ tsp. oregano
Dash of salt

Mix the beans, onion flakes, and celery in bowl. In another bowl, combine the salad dressing mix with the buttermilk. Add the rest of the ingredients. Pour this mixture over the beans and toss lightly. Chill the bean salad for several hours before serving.

Makes 8 servings

	Calories	Carbo-hydrate (gm)	Protein (gm)	Total Fat (gm)	Saturated Fat (gm)	Cholesterol (mg)
Total	313.3	63.8	21.1	0.3	0.0	5.0
Per Serving	39.2	8.0	2.6	0.0	0.0	0.6

Snappy Bleu Cheese Dressing

¾ cup diet mayonnaise
¾ cup plain low-fat
    yogurt
3 oz. bleu cheese,
    crumbled
2 tbsp. vinegar

1 tsp. Worcester-
    shire sauce
½ tsp. salt or garlic
    salt
⅛ tsp. pepper

Combine all the ingredients well and chill before serving.   *Makes 28 tablespoons (14 servings)*

	Calories	Carbo-hydrate (gm)	Protein (gm)	Total Fat (gm)	Saturated Fat (gm)	Choles-terol (mg)
Total	650.8	26.8	24.0	54.0	16.5	183.0
Per Serving	46.5	1.9	1.7	3.9	1.2	13.1

Lemon Zing Dressing

1 tsp. unflavored
    gelatin
1 tbsp. cold water
¼ cup boiling water
½ tsp. garlic salt

½ cup freshly
    squeezed lemon
    juice
Dash red pepper
1 tsp. prepared
    mustard
½ tsp. Worcester-
    shire sauce

Sprinkle the gelatin over the cold water in a cup to soften it. When the gelatin has softened, place it in a bowl and add the boiling water, stirring until the gelatin is completely dissolved. Then beat in the remaining ingredients. The dressing should be stored in the refrigerator but served at room temperature.

Makes 16 tablespoons (8 servings)

	Calories	Carbo-hydrate (gm)	Protein (gm)	Total Fat (gm)	Saturated Fat (gm)	Choles-terol (mg)
Total	38.3	10.0	2.5	0.0	0.0	0.0
Per Serving	4.8	1.3	0.3	0.0	0.0	0.0

The Best Vegetable Dishes

Vegetables, unfortunately, are victims of their own virtue. Anything that is good for you is bound to be a bore — or so it must seem if you grew up in a home where clean plates were equated with godliness.

Many an adult aversion to vegetables got its start when Mama began negotiating deals over parsnips, and pudding: "Finish your spinach or you don't get any pie." Right then and there Junior decided that dessert must be more valuable than vegetables and that when he grew up to be an insurance salesman, nobody was going to dictate how much broccoli he had to eat before starting on the seven-layer cake. As a result, many an otherwise intelligent and mature adult still operates on a two-year-old level where vegetables are concerned, insisting that he dislikes varieties he may never have even tried or tasted.

Maybe Mother's vegetables tasted awful because she didn't know how to cook them. Most people and most restaurants don't. If you have never tried a certain vegetable or have tried it only once, or only one way, you haven't given it a fair chance. You may be depriving yourself of a food friend that can stand you in good stead for the rest of your slim days.

Become a Vegetable Adventurer

- Try a new variety every week. When you shop, look for a vegetable you have never tried before and give it a go.
- Combine vegetables. Put together a blend of old favorites with a vegetable you've never tasted or one you decided you disliked back when you were 10 years old.
- Try a vegetable raw if it is usually served cooked. Or cook a vegetable that is normally served in salad — braised celery or raw mushrooms for example.
- Try vegetables in season, preferably from a local farm. The deteriorated taste and texture of stored or processed produce may be what turns you off.
- Stir-fry vegetables the Oriental way. One tablespoon of diet margarine (50 calories) is all you need to stir up a skilletful of crisp onions and green beans laced with soy sauce.
- Simmer vegetables in soup or stock from which you have skimmed the fat.
- Try cooking vegetables in dry wine. The alcohol calories evaporate.
- Add perennial favorites like chopped onions or sliced green pepper for a fresh taste, especially when cooking canned or frozen vegetables.
- Cook vegetables in canned unsweetened fruit juice. Apple, orange, and pineapple are some you might try.
- Turn the cooking water into a low-cal sauce. Stir a little flour into skim milk and stir it into the saucepan after the vegetables are cooked. A cream sauce without the cream — or cream calories.
- Spice and season your vegetables by adding a small amount of bottled diet dressing to the cooking water. The water evaporates as the vegetables simmer and leaves behind a tangy sauce — no butter needed.

Vegetables Do's and Don'ts

- Do use a sharp knife when preparing vegetables for fewer bruises and less loss of nutrients.

- Don't pare, peel, slice, or cut up fresh vegetables until just before cooking to preserve nutrients.
- Do use as little water as possible to retain both flavor and nutrients. If possible, cook vegetables in so little water that no draining is needed and no vitamins are lost. But watch the pot carefully so they don't stick.
- Don't overcook vegetables. Almost every vegetable is better undercooked and still crunchy.
- Do use a pot with a tight-fitting lid to steam green vegetables.
- Do keep the heat low when steaming vegetables. Otherwise, the steam will escape.
- Do steam white, yellow, and red vegetables. Place them on a rack over boiling water, and cover the pot with a tight lid. This method takes longer than boiling the vegetables, but is well worth it in the savings of nutrients.
- Do add ½ to 1 teaspoon salt to the pot for each six servings of vegetables. Try seasoned salts like butter, onion, garlic, or celery. A little butter-flavored salt added to the cooking water gives vegetables a buttery flavor without the butter or the butter calories.
- Don't use baking soda for preserving color while cooking vegetables. It makes them mushy and flavorless. You can preserve color by undercooking.
- Do cook strong-flavored vegetables like cabbage, broccoli, cauliflower, brussels sprouts, and turnips in an uncovered pan. Add water if needed to prevent burning.
- Do add butter-flavored salt and freshly ground pepper to vegetables just before serving. Herbs and spices as seasonings go a long way, and the calorie contribution is fractional.

Recipes

Spring Artichoke Hearts

9-oz. pkg. frozen artichoke hearts	½ tsp. salt
3 cups thinly sliced celery	10-oz. pkg. frozen peas
½ cup boiling water	2 tsp. lemon juice
	¼ tsp. butter salt

Cook the artichokes and celery in a covered saucepan for 3 minutes in boiling water to which the salt has been added. Add the peas and return to boiling. Cover the pot and cook the vegetables for 5 minutes more. Drain them well. Add the lemon juice and butter salt before serving.   *Makes 8 servings*

	Calories	Carbo-hydrate (gm)	Protein (gm)	Total Fat (gm)	Saturated Fat (gm)	Choles-terol (mg)
Total	305.0	77.8	21.7	0.0	0.0	0.0
Per Serving	38.1	9.7	2.7	0.0	0.0	0.0

Asparagus Stir-Fry

½ cup chicken broth	½ cup chopped onion
1 tbsp. cornstarch	1 lb. fresh asparagus, sliced diagonally
2 tbsp. soy sauce	
1 tbsp. diet margarine	

Skim the fat from the broth by chilling it until the fat rises to the top and can be whisked away. Mix the broth, cornstarch, and soy sauce together in a bowl.

Set the bowl aside. Melt the margarine in a nonstick skillet and sauté the onion until it is golden brown. Add the asparagus and stir-fry it for 3 minutes. Add the broth mixture. Cook and stir until the sauce is clear.

Makes 4 servings

	Calories	Carbo-hydrate (gm)	Protein (gm)	Total Fat (gm)	Saturated Fat (gm)	Choles-terol (mg)
Total	218.8	30.7	14.4	6.0	1.0	18.3
Per Serving	54.7	7.7	3.6	1.5	0.3	4.6

Canadian Green Beans

1 lb. fresh green beans, French-cut, or 9-oz. pkg. frozen beans
¼ cup boiling water
1 tbsp. diet margarine
½ cup finely diced Canadian bacon
1 clove garlic, minced
½ tsp. salt
¼ tsp. pepper
1 tomato, cut in wedges

Cook the fresh or frozen green beans in the water until they are tender. Then drain them. Melt the margarine in a nonstick skillet and sauté the bacon and garlic until they are brown. Add the beans, salt, and pepper to the skillet, and top with the tomato wedges. Cover the pan and heat the contents through.

Makes 4 servings

Hint: The calorie-conscious cook can save 50 calories (about 12 per serving) by omitting the diet margarine. Spray a nonstick skillet with spray-on vegetable coating, so you can brown the bacon and garlic without calories.

	Calories	Carbo-hydrate (gm)	Protein (gm)	Total Fat (gm)	Saturated Fat (gm)	Choles-terol (mg)
Total	351.1	25.0	25.1	18.5	4.3	58.9
Per Serving	87.8	6.3	6.3	4.6	1.1	14.7

gm = grams; mg = milligrams. Nutritional figures are approximate. Figures are based on findings of U.S. Department of Agriculture.

Creamed Broccoli

1 bunch fresh broccoli
(2 pkg. frozen)
1/4 cup boiling salted
water
1/3 cup diet mayonnaise

1/3 cup plain low-fat
yogurt
1 tsp. onion flakes
Dash cayenne
3/4 tsp. salt

Cook the broccoli, covered, in the boiling salted water
until it is barely tender. In a bowl, combine the mayonnaise, yogurt, onion flakes, cayenne, and salt. Serve
the sauce over the hot broccoli. *Makes 4 servings*

	Calories	Carbo-hydrate (gm)	Protein (gm)	Total Fat (gm)	Saturated Fat (gm)	Choles-terol (mg)
Total	362.5	47.9	30.8	16.7	0.7	49.2
Per Serving	90.6	12.0	7.7	4.2	0.2	12.3

Chinese Broccoli with Mushrooms

2 pkg. (10-oz.) frozen
broccoli, partially
thawed
1 tsp. arrowroot or
cornstarch
1/2 cup cold water

1 tsp. beef bouillon
or 1 bouillon
cube
1 tbsp. soy sauce
1 small onion, sliced
8-oz. can mushroom
stems and
pieces

If broccoli spears are used, slice them into 1-inch
diagonal pieces. Combine the arrowroot (or cornstarch) in a saucepan with the water, bouillon, and soy
sauce. Bring the mixture to a boil and then add the rest
of the ingredients. Cook and stir the vegetables over
moderate heat, uncovered, for about 2 minutes until
the sauce thickens and simmers and the vegetables
are just crunchy. Serve immediately. *Makes 6 servings*

	Calories	Carbo-hydrate (gm)	Protein (gm)	Total Fat (gm)	Saturated Fat (gm)	Choles-terol (mg)
Total	265.6	47.1	29.8	4.2	0.0	3.0
Per Serving	44.3	7.9	5.0	0.7	0.0	0.5

Pineapple Carrots

3 cups sliced carrots,
fresh or frozen
6-oz. can unsweetened
pineapple juice
½ tsp. arrowroot or
cornstarch

½ cup water
¼ tsp. cinnamon
¼ tsp. salt
Dash pepper

Combine all the ingredients in a saucepan. Cover the pan tightly and simmer until the carrots are nearly tender. Then uncover the pan and continue to simmer, stirring occasionally, until nearly all of the liquid has evaporated. *Makes 4 servings*

	Calories	Carbo-hydrate (gm)	Protein (gm)	Total Fat (gm)	Saturated Fat (gm)	Choles-terol (mg)
Total	224.9	56.4	6.8	0.0	0.0	0.0
Per Serving	56.2	14.1	1.7	0.0	0.0	0.0

California Carrots with Orange Glaze

4 cups sliced carrots
(fresh or frozen)
1 tsp. butter-flavored
salt
¾ cup water
4 tbsp. defrosted
unsweetened
orange juice
concentrate,
undiluted

1 tbsp. arrowroot
¼ tsp. salt
⅛ tsp. pepper
Cinnamon to taste

Cook carrots in salted water about 10 to 15 minutes, just until tender. Drain the cooking water into a measuring cup. Add the juice concentrate and water to the measuring cup to make a total of 1¼ cups liquid. Stir the arrowroot into this liquid until well blended. Pour the liquid over the carrots in the saucepan. Cook and stir over low heat until sauce simmers and thickens. Season with salt, pepper and cinnamon.

Makes 8 servings

	Calories	Carbo-hydrate (gm)	Protein (gm)	Total Fat (gm)	Saturated Fat (gm)	Choles-terol (mg)
Total	305.9	75.3	9.6	0.0	0.0	0.0
Per Serving	38.1	9.4	1.2	0.0	0.0	0.0

Gourmet Cauliflower

2 pkg. (10-oz.) frozen
  cauliflower, cooked
1/4 tsp. salt
Dash pepper
Dash paprika

1/2 cup nondairy low-
  fat sour cream
  substitute
4 tbsp. bread crumbs

Place the cauliflower in a nonstick baking dish and
season it with salt, pepper, and paprika. Cover it with
the imitation sour cream and bread crumbs and bake
in a preheated 350° oven just until brown.

Makes 6 servings

	Calories	Carbo-hydrate (gm)	Protein (gm)	Total Fat (gm)	Saturated Fat (gm)	Choles-terol (mg)
Total	434.3	50.2	21.8	20.3	17.8	1.3
Per Serving	72.4	8.4	3.6	3.4	3.0	0.2

Easy Cheesy Cauliflower

10 3/4-oz. can condensed
  cheddar cheese
  soup
1/4 cup skim milk

Generous dash
  nutmeg
2 pkg. (10-oz.) frozen
  cauliflower,
  cooked and
  drained

Blend the soup, milk, and nutmeg in a saucepan. Cook
and stir the sauce until it is bubbling. Pour over the hot
cauliflower and serve.

Makes 6 servings

	Calories	Carbo-hydrate (gm)	Protein (gm)	Total Fat (gm)	Saturated Fat (gm)	Choles-terol (mg)
Total	525.8	52.1	29.2	25.8	12.9	65.8
Per Serving	87.6	8.7	5.0	4.3	2.2	11.0

*gm = grams; mg = milligrams. Nutritional figures are approximate.
Figures are based on findings of U.S. Department of Agriculture.*

Easy Eggplant Parmesan

3 tbsp. Italian-seasoned bread crumbs
1½ tbsp. grated Parmesan cheese
½ tsp. garlic salt
Pinch cayenne

1 eggplant, peeled and cubed
8-oz. can tomato sauce
3 thin slices part-skim mozzarella cheese (3 oz.)

Mix the bread crumbs, Parmesan cheese, garlic salt, and cayenne together in a bowl. Arrange the eggplant in the bottom of a baking dish. Spread the bread crumb mixture over this and then pour on the tomato sauce. Top with the slices of mozzarella cheese. Bake in a preheated 350° oven for 25 minutes.

Makes 6 servings

	Calories	Carbo-hydrate (gm)	Protein (gm)	Total Fat (gm)	Saturated Fat (gm)	Choles-terol (mg)
Total	556.6	43.6	65.2	25.4	8.2	82.0
Per Serving	92.8	7.3	10.9	4.2	1.4	13.7

Mushrooms and Onions

1 tbsp. diet margarine
2 small onions, sliced
1 lb. fresh mushrooms

1 tbsp. water
½ tsp. salt
⅛ tsp. ground black pepper

Melt the margarine in a nonstick skillet and sauté the onions until they are limp. Add the mushrooms and water. Cover the pan and simmer 5 minutes. Season with the salt and pepper before serving. *Makes 6 servings*

Note: If fresh mushrooms are not available, you may use 2 cans (6 to 8 oz. each) of whole mushrooms. If you use canned mushrooms, use 1 tablespoon of the liquid from the can instead of 1 tbsp. water.

	Calories	Carbo-hydrate (gm)	Protein (gm)	Total Fat (gm)	Saturated Fat (gm)	Choles-terol (mg)
Total	215.1	30.2	14.9	7.8	1.0	0.0
Per Serving	35.9	5.0	2.5	1.3	0.2	0.0

Summer Squash Bake

2 lb. yellow summer
 squash, sliced in 1/2-
 in. pieces
1/4 cup water
3 tbsp. chopped onion
3 eggs, beaten

1/2 tsp. hot pepper
 sauce
2 tsp. parsley flakes
1 tsp. salt
1/4 tsp. pepper
5 tbsp. cracker
 crumbs

Boil the squash about 3 minutes in the water until it is tender. Drain the squash and add all the remaining ingredients except the cracker crumbs and mix well. Pour the mixture into a 1-quart casserole that has been sprayed with vegetable coating. Sprinkle the cracker crumbs over the top. Bake the casserole uncovered in a preheated 350° oven for 35 to 40 minutes until the squash is brown. *Makes 6 servings*

	Calories	Carbo-hydrate (gm)	Protein (gm)	Total Fat (gm)	Saturated Fat (gm)	Choles-terol (mg)
Total	438.2	41.8	28.2	19.3	6.0	756.0
Per Serving	73.0	7.0	4.7	3.2	1.0	126.0

Baked Tomatoes

2 large ripe tomatoes,
 halved
2 green onions, minced

1 tsp. minced fresh
 parsley
1/4 tsp. salt
Dash pepper

Place each tomato half cut side up on a large square of double-thick foil. Sprinkle the surface of the tomato halves with green onion, parsley, salt, and pepper. Bring the foil up and around the tomato half. Seal the sides of the foil, but leave a space at the top for steam to escape. Bake the tomatoes in a preheated 350° oven for 20 minutes. *Makes 4 servings*

	Calories	Carbo-hydrate (gm)	Protein (gm)	Total Fat (gm)	Saturated Fat (gm)	Choles-terol (mg)
Total	82.2	18.3	4.1	0.0	0.0	0.0
Per Serving	20.6	4.6	1.0	0.0	0.0	0.0

Apple-Glazed Zucchini

2 zucchini (¾ lb.),
sliced
6-oz. can unsweetened
apple juice
½ tsp. arrowroot or
cornstarch

1 tsp. instant dried
onion
½ tsp. dried parsley
flakes
¼ tsp. salt
Dash pepper

Combine all of the ingredients in a shallow saucepan. Simmer the mixture, uncovered, over moderate heat, stirring occasionally, until most of the liquid has evaporated, leaving a thick sauce.   *Makes 4 servings*

	Calories	Carbo-hydrate (gm)	Protein (gm)	Total Fat (gm)	Saturated Fat (gm)	Choles-terol (mg)
Total	145.1	35.4	3.3	0.0	0.0	0.0
Per Serving	36.3	8.9	0.8	0.0	0.0	0.0

Skillet Zucchini Parmesan

2 tbsp. diet margarine
6 medium zucchini,
sliced
¼ tsp. butter-flavored
salt

½ tsp. oregano
½ cup grated
Parmesan
cheese

Melt the margarine in a heavy nonstick skillet. Add the zucchini and season it with salt and oregano. Cover the pan tightly and cook over low heat about 5 minutes, just long enough to heat the slices through. Sprinkle the zucchini with the cheese and serve immediately.   *Makes 12 servings*

	Calories	Carbo-hydrate (gm)	Protein (gm)	Total Fat (gm)	Saturated Fat (gm)	Choles-terol (mg)
Total	904.0	46.8	69.6	55.2	26.0	129.6
Per Serving	75.3	3.9	5.8	4.6	2.2	10.8

---

gm = grams; mg = milligrams. Nutritional figures are approximate. Figures are based on findings of U.S. Department of Agriculture.

Vegetable Medley

1 tbsp. diet margarine
2 cups diagonally
  sliced carrots
2 cups snap beans,
  broken into 1-in.
  pieces

2 cups sliced
  summer squash
1 cup sliced onion
½ tsp. salt
Dash pepper

Melt the margarine in a nonstick skillet. Add the vegetables and salt. Cover the pan, and cook the vegetables, stirring occasionally, 10 to 15 minutes until they are crisp-tender. Season with the pepper according to your taste and serve the vegetables hot.

Makes 6 servings

	Calories	Carbo-hydrate (gm)	Protein (gm)	Total Fat (gm)	Saturated Fat (gm)	Choles-terol (mg)
Total	290.0	58.0	14.0	6.0	1.0	0.0
Per Serving	48.3	9.7	2.3	1.0	0.2	0.0

Mini-Caloried Marinated Vegetables

1 cup crisp-cooked,
  unbuttered green
  beans or other
  vegetable such as
  asparagus,
  broccoli, carrots, or
  cauliflower
1 tbsp. minced onion (1
  tsp. onion flakes)

2 tbsp. low-calorie
  salad dressing
2 tbsp. olive juice
  (from jar of
  olives)
¼ pimiento, diced
  and drained
½ fresh red bell
  pepper, chopped

Combine all ingredients and chill until serving time.

Makes 2 servings

	Calories	Carbo-hydrate (gm)	Protein (gm)	Total Fat (gm)	Saturated Fat (gm)	Choles-terol (mg)
Total	71.8	10.5	2.3	2.0	0.0	0.0
Per Serving	35.9	5.3	1.2	1.0	0.0	0.0

gm = grams; mg = milligrams. Nutritional figures are approximate. Figures are based on findings of U.S. Department of Agriculture.

Skinny Potatoes, Pasta and Rice

If you pass up potatoes, skip spaghetti, or refuse rice in favor of a second helping of steak, you are probably a victim of the carbohydrate myth. Low-carb dieters seem to think some calories are more fattening than others and that somehow they can achieve slimness on limitless meat, cheese, cream, and other high-fat foods. As a matter of fact, the so-called starchy foods are relatively low in calories. Most cost between 70 and 90 calories a serving, considerably less than the second helping of high-fat foods most low-carb dieters would replace them with. In fact, the only time these appetite-appeasers become fattening is when fat is added to them in the form of butter, cream sauce, gravy, cheese, or other calorie-rich toppings. A half-cup serving of mashed potatoes is only 63 calories, but a level tablespoon of butter adds 100 more. Here is just how low-cal most of these palate-pleasers are before the extra calories are added on.

	Serving	Calories
Baked potato	1 medium, no fat	90
Boiled potato	1 medium, peeled	65
Boiled potato	1 medium, unpeeled	76
Mashed potato	½ cup, milk, no fat	63
Spaghetti	½ cup, cooked firm	108
	½ cup, cooked tender	83
Macaroni	½ cup, cooked firm	104
	½ cup, cooked tender	75
Egg noodles	½ cup, cooked	100
Brown rice	½ cup, cooked	89
White rice	½ cup, cooked	82
Long grain rice	½ cup, cooked	79
Instant rice	½ cup, prepared, no fat	80

A frozen stuffed potato is nearly triple the calories of a plain potato. Heat-and-serve fried rice is 40 percent more fattening than regular rice. And macaroni and cheese made from a convenience mix is double the calories of plain pasta. But who wants plain potatoes or naked noodles? In this chapter, we offer a variety of variations from standard fattening recipes all aimed at keeping calorie counts low.

Recipes

Stuffed Potatoes

4 baking potatoes
1 tsp. butter-flavored
   salt
2 egg whites
   Pinch of cream of
   tartar
   Pinch of pepper

1 tsp. freeze-dried
   chives
½ to ¾ cup skim milk
3 tbsp. grated extra-
   sharp cheddar
   cheese
Paprika

Scrub the potatoes, pierce them with a fork and bake them in a preheated 400° oven for about 1 hour until they are soft. Remove the potatoes from the oven and carefully slice them in half, lengthwise. Combine the salt, egg whites, and cream of tartar in a bowl. Using an electric mixer, whip the egg whites until stiff peaks form. Carefully scoop out the pulp of the potatoes and place them in another bowl. Add the pepper and chives and whip them with the electric mixer, adding a little milk at a time until they are fluffy. Fold the egg white mixture into the potatoes and pile the mixture back into the potato skins. Sprinkle the top of each potato with grated cheese and paprika and return the potatoes to the oven. Bake them in a preheated 425° oven until the cheese is melted and the potatoes are hot.   *Makes 8 servings*

	Calories	Carbo-hydrate (gm)	Protein (gm)	Total Fat (gm)	Saturated Fat (gm)	Choles-terol (mg)
Total	686.6	94.8	40.8	18.0	10.0	59.8
Per Serving	85.8	11.9	5.1	2.3	1.3	7.5

Savory Bacon Potatoes

10¾-oz. can condensed
cream of celery
soup
4 tbsp. water
4 tbsp. minced onion
Pinch of pepper

3 potatoes (1lb.
total) peeled,
boiled, cut in
chunks
1 tbsp. bacon-
flavored bits

In a saucepan, combine the soup, water, onion, and pepper. Cook this mixture over low heat for 5 to 10 minutes, stirring occasionally. Then add the potatoes and continue to heat thoroughly. Serve the potatoes garnished with the bacon-flavored bits.

Makes 8 servings

	Calories	Carbo-hydrate (gm)	Protein (gm)	Total Fat (gm)	Saturated Fat (gm)	Choles-terol (mg)
Total	475.3	80.1	11.7	13.1	0.0	18.3
Per Serving	59.4	10.0	1.5	1.6	0.0	2.3

Parsley Potatoes en Casserole

6 potatoes (2 lb. total),
peeled and cubed
4 tbsp. chopped fresh
parsley
2 tbsp. minced green
onion

4 tbsp. lemon juice
1 tsp. grated lemon
peel
1 tsp. butter-flavored
salt

Toss all of the ingredients together and turn the mixture into a nonstick baking dish. Cover the dish, and bake the potatoes in a preheated 425° oven for 45 minutes.

Makes 12 servings

	Calories	Carbo-hydrate (gm)	Protein (gm)	Total Fat (gm)	Saturated Fat (gm)	Choles-terol (mg)
Total	505.3	114.6	12.6	0.0	0.0	0.0
Per Serving	42.1	9.6	1.1	0.0	0.0	0.0

gm = grams; mg = milligrams. Nutritional figures are approximate. Figures are based on findings of U.S. Department of Agriculture.

Shell Salad

4½ tsp. dried onion flakes
2 tbsp. vinegar
1 cup diet mayonnaise
1¾ tsp. salt
¼ tsp. pepper
2 tsp. paprika
8 oz. small shell
  macaroni, cooked
  and drained

3 medium tomatoes,
  cut in wedges
½ cup chopped
  green pepper
2 tbsp. pitted black
  olives, sliced
3 hard-cooked eggs,
  sliced
2 tbsp. snipped
  parsley

Combine the onion and vinegar and let it stand for a few minutes. Then add the mayonnaise, salt, pepper, and paprika and mix well. Mix the macaroni, tomatoes, green pepper, and olives in a large salad bowl; and pour the mayonnaise mixture over all. Toss lightly. Chill the salad for several hours before serving. When serving, garnish with the egg slices and parsley.

Makes 8 servings

	Calories	Carbo-hydrate (gm)	Protein (gm)	Total Fat (gm)	Saturated Fat (gm)	Choles-terol (mg)
Total	985.0	102.3	33.0	55.7	6.0	884.0
Per Serving	164.2	17.1	5.5	9.3	1.0	147.3

Spaghetti and Meatballs

¾ lb. extra-lean round
  steak, ground
½ tsp. oregano
1 tsp. basil
½ tsp. salt
  Pepper to taste
1 cup water
1-lb. 3-oz. can Italian
  tomatoes,
  undrained
6-oz. can tomato paste
1 cup chopped onion

1 green pepper,
  chopped
1 tbsp. oregano or
  mixed herbs
1 garlic clove,
  minced
½ cup chopped
  celery
6 cups tender-
  cooked
  spaghetti

Combine the meat with the oregano, basil, salt, and pepper. Shape the mixture into 18 small meatballs, and brown them under the broiler, turning them once. In a large saucepan bring all of the remaining ingredients (except the spaghetti) to a boil. Add the meatballs; cover the pot and simmer over low heat for 1 hour or longer. Pour sauce over spaghetti. *Makes 6 servings*

	Calories	Carbo-hydrate (gm)	Protein (gm)	Total Fat (gm)	Saturated Fat (gm)	Choles-terol (mg)
Total	1787.6	260.0	148.7	21.5	4.4	315.2
Per Serving	297.9	43.4	24.8	3.6	0.7	52.5

Italian Pasta Soup

2 cans chicken broth
½ cup chopped onion
½ tsp. oregano

1 cup chopped canned tomatoes, undrained
1 tbsp. chopped parsley
¼ cup uncooked elbow macaroni

Skim the fat from the broth by using a bulb-type baster. In a large saucepan combine all of the ingredients except the macaroni. Bring the mixture to a boil. Then add the macaroni. Cook over low heat until the macaroni is tender, stirring ccasionally.

Makes 6 servings

	Calories	Carbo-hydrate (gm)	Protein (gm)	Total Fat (gm)	Saturated Fat (gm)	Choles-terol (mg)
Total	273.5	43.4	21.6	1.6	0.0	73.6
Per Serving	45.6	7.2	3.6	0.3	0.0	12.3

gm = grams; mg = milligrams. Nutritional figures are approximate. Figures are based on findings of U.S. Department of Agriculture.

Wild Rice and Mushrooms

10½-oz. can condensed beef or chicken broth

4-oz. can sliced mushrooms, drained reserving liquid

2 medium onions, chopped

½ cup wild rice

1 cup long-grain rice

2 tbsp. parsley

Skim the broth with a bulb-type baster; or chill until the fat rises and can be whisked away. Combine the broth with enough water to equal 2 cups. Bring the broth, mushroom liquid, and onions to a boil in a saucepan. Add the wild rice, reduce the heat, and simmer about 20 minutes. Then add the long-grain rice and mushrooms. Return the mixture to boiling. Again, reduce heat and simmer about 20 minutes until the rice is tender. Serve garnished with parsley. *Makes 10 servings*

	Calories	Carbo-hydrate (gm)	Protein (gm)	Total Fat (gm)	Saturated Fat (gm)	Choles-terol (mg)
Total	1179.1	249.2	44.9	1.5	0.0	55.7
Per Serving	117.9	24.9	4.5	0.2	0.0	5.6

Slender Rice

1 cup finely minced celery

¼ cup finely minced onion

1 cup water

1 cup quick or instant rice

½ tsp. salt or butter-flavored salt

⅛ tsp. pepper

The celery and onion should be chopped as fine as the grains of rice. Combine all of the ingredients in a covered saucepan and simmer for 2 minutes. Remove the pan from the heat, and set it aside for 5 minutes or more, until serving time. *Makes 6 servings*

	Calories	Carbo-hydrate (gm)	Protein (gm)	Total Fat (gm)	Saturated Fat (gm)	Choles-terol (mg)
Total	205.0	48.5	4.5	0.0	0.0	0.0
Per Serving	34.2	8.1	0.8	0.0	0.0	0.0

Meat Facts and Fallacies

Meat! What red-blooded American doesn't love it? If you're like most homemakers, meat is the most expensive item in your food budget. It may also be the most costly category in your calorie budget. Many well-intentioned but misinformed dieters are wasting their money and calories on meat — too much and the wrong kind — in the mistaken notion that a high-meat diet is necessary to achieve slimness. Meat is good, yes. But too much of a good thing is not only fattening, it's boring!

How many of these fallacies about meat do you believe?

Fallacy: Meat is all protein, and the more you eat, the thinner you'll be.

Fact: Meat is only part protein. The rest is fat, and fat is the most fattening basic food there is. Some of the most popular cuts of meat have nearly five times as many fat calories as protein calories. And the more calories you eat, the fatter you'll be.

Fallacy: You need meat every day.

Fact: Other animal foods are an equal or better source of complete protein. Eggs, skim milk, cottage cheese and yogurt are low-fat, low-calorie foods that are extra-rich in protein. Eight ounces of 99 percent fat-free cottage cheese alone is enough to satisfy most people's daily protein needs. Remember, meat is also balanced by the smaller amounts of less complete protein found in vegetable foods. Nuts and beans are especially rich in vegetable protein. And soy products such as soy flours, protein-enriched mixes and meat extenders are particularly important sources of inexpensive, low-calorie protein.

Fallacy: You can never eat too much meat.

Fact: Some steak-lovers may feel that way, but a superabundance of protein, especially meat protein, can be harmful. Meat contains cholesterol and saturated fat that have been implicated in heart disease. Too much protein in the diet is especially bad for anyone with latent kidney trouble. Recent studies have demonstrated that high-protein diets can upset calcium balance and accelerate osteoporosis, loss of bone tissue.

Fallacy: Simple steaks and roasts are better for calorie counters than combination dishes like stews or casseroles.

Fact: The cuts of meat most amenable to simple broiling or roasting are generally the most expensive, in calories as well as cost, while the leanest and least costly cuts are ideally suited to imaginative combinations and gourmet creations. And, since most of the other ingredients in casseroles are less fattening than meat, combination dishes allow dieters to satisfy their appetites with fewer calories. Of course, it's necessary to prepare these dishes in a way that eliminates excess fat.

Fallacy: Rare meat is less fattening than meat that is well done.

Fact: The longer meat is cooked, the more fat is melted out and eliminated, presuming that the fat is drained away or skimmed off. This does not mean that you should overcook an expensive porterhouse, but rather that you should concentrate on the less expensive, less fattening cuts, the kinds that are usually slow-simmered to a well-done tenderness.

Fallacy: Fat meat is juicy; lean meat is dry.

Fact: Fat meat is greasy, and because of its greasiness, fatty meat is better able to withstand the mishandling of too-high temperatures. Too-quick cooking at too-high temperatures robs lean meat of its juiciness.

Fallacy: Beef is less fattening than most other meats.

Fact: Many cuts of lamb, pork, and ham are lower in fat and calories than the most popular cuts of beef. Veal, poultry, and seafood are much more slimming.

How to Cook Meat

Broiling is the dry-heat method for quick cooking. When broiling, the heat source is above the meat.

1. Set your oven regulator for broiling, the highest heat.
2. Place the meat on a rack in your broiler pan 3 to 6 inches away from the heat. Thick cuts of meat should be placed further away from the heat.
3. Broil the meat until the top side is brown.
4. Sprinkle the browned surface with salt, pepper, and any other seasonings you desire.
5. Turn the meat and brown the other side. Make a small cut in the center of the meat to see if the desired doneness has been reached.

Barbecuing is another form of dry-heat cookery, usually done outdoors over glowing charcoal. Electric and gas barbecues are also available; some are built right into the kitchen. In barbecuing, the source of heat is beneath the meat. For best results, the meat should not be closer than 3 inches from the heat. When the meat is brown on one side, turn it with tongs and brown the other side.

Pan-broiling is yet another dry-heat method of cooking.

1. Place the meat in an uncovered nonstick skillet or griddle.
2. The pan may be sprinkled with a thin layer of salt or sprayed with vegetable coating for nonstick cooking. Do not add fat or water. Do not cover the pan.
3. Cook slowly over low heat, turning the meat occasionally.
4. Pour off or remove all fat as it accumulates.
5. Brown the meat on both sides, being careful not to overcook it.

6. Season the meat and serve it at once.

Oven-roasting is the slow method of dry cooking.

1. To achieve tenderness with lean cuts, treat the meat with meat tenderizer according to package directions; or for a more interesting flavor, marinate the meat for several hours.

2. Place the meat on a rack in an open shallow roasting pan.

3. Insert a meat thermometer so that the bulb or tip of the thermometer is in the center of the meat.

4. Do not add water and do not cover the pan.

5. Roast the meat in a slow oven, approximately 325°, to the desired degree of doneness. If you like your beef rare, roast it until the thermometer reads 140°; if medium is your taste, the thermometer should read 160°. Never allow the thermometer to reach more than 170°. Lamb is rare at 165° to 170°; medium at 174°; and well done at 180°. Pork should be roasted to an internal temperature of 170°.

6. Let the roast stand about 10 minutes before carving.

Braising or pot-roasting is the preferred method of moist-heat cooking. It is particularly suitable for less tender cuts of beef.

1. Brown the meat slowly on all sides in a heavy nonstick utensil without added fat. One low-cal method of browning is to add a tablespoon of water to the meat, cover the utensil, and heat it slowly over moderate heat. The water will evaporate, and the steam will cause the meat to release its own inner fat. Then, uncover the pot and let the meat brown in its own fat. The meat may also be browned under the broiler.

2. If you like, season the meat with salt, pepper, herbs, and spices.

3. Add a small amount of liquid such as water, wine, tomato juice, or fruit juice to the meat.

4. Cover the pot tightly, and cook the meat at a low temperature until it is tender.

5. You can make a sauce or gravy from the liquid in the pot if you like, but first skim the fat from the pan juices.

6. Pot roast is best made a day ahead, then refriger-

ated until about half-hour before serving time. The refrigeration will cause the fat that rises to the top to harden so it can be lifted off and discarded before the meat is reheated.

Simmering is another method of moist-heat cooking. This method requires more liquid than others and is used with cuts of meat that need longer cooking and more moisture to make them fork-tender.

1. If desired, brown the meat on all sides in a non-stick utensil without added fat. (See step 1 under Braising).

2. Cover the meat with water or other liquid like wine or juice.

3. Season with salt, pepper, herbs, and spices if you like.

4. Cover the pot and simmer the meat until it is tender. Do not boil.

5. For best results, cook the meat the day before serving and chill it overnight in the stock in which it was cooked. The fat will float to the top and harden, so it can be easily removed before reheating and serving the meat.

6. When vegetables are to be cooked with the meat, add them whole or in pieces after the fat has been removed, and cook them just until they are tender.

What's Your Beef?

Beef is America's favorite food. From filet mignon to hamburger to stew, beef proves its great versatility. You can boil it, broil it, braise it, fry it, and even eat it raw. And it is available in a wide range of prices. Fortunately for the weight-conscious millions, it is the less expensive cuts of beef that are the calorie bargains. Part of what makes prime beef "prime" is the marbling of fat throughout the meat — great for flavor, lousy for waistlines.

Recipes

Pot Roast Olé

2 tsp. diet margarine
4-lb. lean boneless
   bottom round,
   trimmed of fat and
   rolled for pot roast
1/2 cup water

1 tsp. chili powder
1 tbsp. paprika
2 tsp. onion salt
1/8 tsp. ground clove
1/2 tsp. cinnamon
2 tbsp. flour

Melt margarine over low heat in a heavy, nonstick Dutch oven. Brown the meat slowly on all sides in the melted margarine. Add the water and seasonings to the pot. Cover and simmer the meat slowly about 2 1/2 to 3 hours until tender. Remove the meat to a platter, and keep it warm.

Pour the pan drippings into a large measuring cup. Add water and ice cubes to bring it to 2 cups. When the ice cubes have melted and the fat has risen to the surface, skim off all the fat. Stir the flour into the cold drippings, and return it to the pot. Over low heat, cook and stir the liquid, scraping the pan well, until it simmers and thickens.   *Makes 12 servings*

	Calories	Carbo-hydrate (gm)	Protein (gm)	Total Fat (gm)	Saturated Fat (gm)	Choles-terol (mg)
Total	3121.7	12.4	570.5	83.2	25.7	1682.7
Per Serving	260.1	1.0	47.5	6.9	2.1	140.2

Cider-Spicy Pot Roast

3-lb. boneless top round
  roast, bottom or
  eye, trimmed of fat
1/4 cup cider vinegar
1 cup unsweetened
  cider

2 tbsp. mixed
  pickling spices
2 tsp. salt
1/8 tsp. pepper

Place the meat in a bowl. Combine all the other ingredients and pour over the meat. Cover the bowl and
refrigerate for 24 hours. Transfer the meat and liquid
into a heavy pot or Dutch oven. Simmer it over low
heat, covered, for about 2 1/2 hours until the meat is
tender; or roast it, covered, in a 350° oven for about 2 1/2
hours. Remove the meat to a serving platter. Using a
bulb-type baster, skim all of the fat from the pan drippings. Simmer the remaining liquid, uncovered, until it
is reduced to just enough to pour over the meat. Strain
the reduced liquid, pour over the meat and serve.

Makes 10 servings

	Calories	Carbo-hydrate (gm)	Protein (gm)	Total Fat (gm)	Saturated Fat (gm)	Choles-terol (mg)
Total	2344.5	32.2	426.9	53.3	17.8	1262.4
Per Serving	234.5	3.2	42.7	5.3	1.8	126.2

Slim-but-Saucy Pot Roast

3-lb. beef arm pot roast,
  trimmed of fat
2 tsp. salt
1/8 tsp. pepper
2 medium onions,
  sliced
1/2 can (10 3/4-oz.)
  condensed cheddar
  cheese soup

8-oz. can tomato
  sauce
4-oz. can mushroom
  stems and
  pieces,
  undrained
1/4 tsp. oregano
1/4 tsp. basil

Place the pot roast in a nonstick roasting pan and
roast it, uncovered, in a preheated 475° oven just until

the meat is browned. Pour off the pan drippings that have accumulated and lower the oven temperature to 325°. Season the meat with the salt and pepper, and add the onions, cheese soup, tomato sauce, mushrooms, oregano, and basil to the pan. Cover the pan tightly, and roast the meat slowly for about 2½ hours until it is tender. To serve, slice the meat thinly.

Makes 10 servings

	Calories	Carbohydrate (gm)	Protein (gm)	Total Fat (gm)	Saturated Fat (gm)	Cholesterol (mg)
Total	2574.9	51.5	442.4	65.7	23.8	1292.4
Per Serving	257.5	5.2	44.2	6.6	2.4	129.2

Côte d'Azur Steak en Brochette

2 lb. lean top round steak, trimmed of fat and cubed
1 cup diet Italian salad dressing

2 medium zucchini, cut in 1-in. slices
12 cherry tomatoes

Combine the beef cubes and dressing in a bowl, coating the meat thoroughly. Cover the meat tightly and refrigerate 10 hours or overnight, stirring once or twice. Drain the marinade from the meat, but reserve it. Thread 4 metal skewers alternately with the beef cubes, zucchini, and tomatoes. Brush with the marinade. Place the kebabs over hot coals and broil them 12 to 18 minutes, depending upon degree of doneness desired, turning and brushing them with the marinade occasionally.

Makes 8 servings

	Calories	Carbohydrate (gm)	Protein (gm)	Total Fat (gm)	Saturated Fat (gm)	Cholesterol (mg)
Total	2133.3	61.6	294.1	69.3	26.7	826.5
Per Serving	266.7	7.7	36.8	8.7	3.3	103.3

---

gm = grams; mg = milligrams. Nutritional figures are approximate. Figures are based on findings of U.S. Department of Agriculture.

Rare Roast Beef with Teriyaki Sauce

3-lb. lean boneless arm
   roast, trimmed of fat
Meat tenderizer
Monosodium
   glutamate

1 cup unsweetened
   cider
4 tbsp. soy sauce
1 tbsp. cornstarch
1/4 cup cold water

Sprinkle the meat with tenderizer and monosodium glutamate. Puncture well with a fork. Put the roast in a plastic bag and set it in a shallow dish. Combine the cider and soy sauce and pour into the bag. Secure the bag with a twist-tie and cover all surfaces of the meat with marinade. Refrigerate 8 hours or longer, up to two days.

Empty the meat and marinade into a small ovenproof baking dish. Insert a meat thermometer into the meat. Bake uncovered at 275° until thermometer indicates 140° for rare, or 150° to 160° for medium, about 2 hours. Don't overcook! Drain the liquid from the pan into a tall glass. Spoon off all fat that rises to the surface. Pour the liquid into a saucepan and heat to boiling. Combine the cornstarch and cold water and stir into the hot liquid. Cook and stir until thickened. Brown the surface of the meat briefly under the broiler. Slice the meat thinly against the grain and serve with sauce.

Makes 10 servings

	Calories	Carbo-hydrate (gm)	Protein (gm)	Total Fat (gm)	Saturated Fat (gm)	Choles-terol (mg)
Total	2404.4	39.5	430.7	53.3	17.8	1262.3
Per Serving	240.4	4.0	43.1	5.3	1.8	126.2

Savory Swiss Steak

1 tbsp. diet margarine
2-lb. boneless round
   steak, trimmed of
   fat
1 tsp. garlic salt
1/8 tsp. pepper

1 cup chopped
   onions
3 cups canned
   stewed tomatoes
1 cup chopped
   celery

Place the margarine in a nonstick skillet and melt over moderate heat. Add the steak to the pan. Season the meat with the garlic salt and pepper. Raise the heat under the pan to high and brown the meat quickly on both sides. Lower the heat, and before going any further, pour off any fat that has accumulated in the pan. Then add the onions, tomatoes, and celery to the meat and cover the skillet tightly. Simmer — do not boil — over very low heat for 1½ hours or more until the meat is tender and the sauce is thick.

Makes 8 servings

	Calories	Carbo-hydrate (gm)	Protein (gm)	Total Fat (gm)	Saturated Fat (gm)	Choles-terol (mg)
Total	1987.9	46.0	287.9	62.3	27.7	826.5
Per Serving	248.5	5.8	36.0	7.8	3.5	103.3

Smothered Baked Steak

3-lb. lean beef round steak, cut 2-in. thick and trimmed of fat
½ tsp. salt
¼ tsp. pepper
1 cup unsweetened pineapple juice
6-oz. can tomato paste

3 tbsp. Worcester-shire sauce
2 tbsp. lemon juice
1 clove garlic, minced
4-oz. can sliced mushrooms
2 large onions, sliced

Place the steak on a rack in a shallow roasting pan; brown under the broiler. Drain the fat. Season with salt and pepper. Combine all the other ingredients. Pour over the meat. Roast uncovered in a preheated 325° oven for 1½ to 2 hours. Cut the meat diagonally. Serve with the pan juices.

Makes 12 servings

	Calories	Carbo-hydrate (gm)	Protein (gm)	Total Fat (gm)	Saturated Fat (gm)	Choles-terol (mg)
Total	3022 7	102.0	434.7	80.0	40.0	1240.0
Per serving	251.9	8.5	36.2	6.7	3.3	103.3

---

gm = grams; mg = milligrams. Nutritional figures are approximate. Figures are based on findings of U.S. Department of Agriculture.

Harvest Stew

1 tbsp. flour
1 tsp. garlic salt
1/4 tsp. pepper
1-lb. lean boneless bottom round steak, trimmed of fat and cut in 1-in. cubes
1 tbsp. safflower or corn oil
1 onion, chopped

1 cup beef broth, bouillon, or water
1/2 cup dry red wine
1 rutabaga (yellow turnip), pared and diced to make 2 cups
3 to 4 carrots, pared and diced
1 tsp. parsley flakes
1/4 to 1/2 tsp. crushed thyme

Mix the flour, salt, and pepper together in a paper bag. Add the meat. Shake a few pieces at a time until all are coated. Heat the oil in a heavy, nonstick Dutch oven. Brown the meat in the hot oil. Add the onion, broth, and wine to the pot, cover it tightly, and simmer the meat slowly for 1 1/2 hours or until it is tender. Skim off the fat from the pan drippings by using a bulb-type baster. Add the rutabaga, carrots, parsley flakes, and thyme to the pot. Cover and simmer for an additional 30 minutes or until the vegetables are nearly tender. Uncover the pot and continue to simmer the meat and vegetables until most of the liquid has evaporated.

Makes 4 servings

	Calories	Carbo-hydrate (gm)	Protein (gm)	Total Fat (gm)	Saturated Fat (gm)	Choles-terol (mg)
Total	1180.4	52.0	154.8	31.9	6.9	445.0
Per Serving	295.1	13.0	38.7	8.0	1.7	111.3

Luscious Veal

Unlike luxury foods, veal is one extravagance the calorie counter can afford — if the budget permits. While the price per pound is high compared with other meats, veal is actually a better bargain than simple price comparisons might indicate. Veal's relative lack of fat (and fat calories) means a corresponding increase in protein content. And protein, after all, is why you feed your family meat in the first place.

Veal, of course, is baby beef. The best veal comes from animals 4 to 14 weeks old, weighing 100 pounds or less. Because of its tender age, veal is naturally tasty and tender without the fatty marbling of mature beef.

Compare the calorie, fat, and protein content of similar cuts of beef and veal, and you'll see why veal is often a better buy for dieters.

BEEF AND VEAL COMPARISONS

	Protein	Fat	Calories*
Veal chuck	19%	10%	173
Beef chuck	16%	31%	352
Veal rib chops	19%	14%	207
Beef rib steak	14%	43%	444
Veal loin chops	19%	11%	181
Beef porterhouse	15%	36%	390
Veal shank	20%	8%	156
Beef shank	18%	23%	289
Veal rump	19%	9%	164
Beef rump	17%	25%	303

*Per 100 grams (approximately 3½ ounces). All data approximate, adapted from U.S. Department of Agriculture information.

Veal's sophisticated flavor is subtly accented by the judicious use of lemon or wine and herbs, or garlic, cheese, and tomato for more robust dishes. Because of its leanness, veal is at its best when gently cooked; scallopini sautéed lightly in a nonstick skillet, for example, or a tender, rolled rump slow-roasted at low temperature. The less tender cuts of veal can be creatively seasoned and slow-simmered in wine or tomato juice. Under no circumstances, however, should veal be carelessly tossed into a hot frying pan, seared in a hot oven, or scorched under the broiler. Only the tiniest, most tender chops can be broiled or barbecued and then only with patience and care.

Recipes

Veal Goulash

1 tbsp. diet margarine	1½ tsp. salt
2-lb. lean veal shoulder, trimmed of fat and cut in 1-in. cubes	1 tbsp. paprika
	¼ tsp. pepper
2 onions, sliced	1 tsp. caraway seeds
16-oz. can whole peeled Italian tomatoes in purée	

Melt the margarine in a large nonstick skillet. Brown the meat slowly in the melted margarine; then add the remaining ingredients. Heat the mixture to boiling. Then lower the heat, cover the pan and simmer for 1¼ hours, or until the meat is tender. *Makes 8 servings*

	Calories	Carbo-hydrate (gm)	Protein (gm)	Total Fat (gm)	Saturated Fat (gm)	Choles-terol (mg)
Total	1414.4	40.0	189.4	50.7	22.3	640.2
Per Serving	176.8	5.0	23.7	6.3	2.8	80.0

gm = grams; mg = milligrams. Nutritional figures are approximate. Figures are based on findings of U.S. Department of Agriculture

Veal Provencal Petite

10½-oz. can chicken consommé
8-oz. can boiled whole onions
8-oz. can small carrots
8-oz. can potatoes
4-oz. can mushroom caps
2 tsp. diet margarine

1 lb. lean boneless veal, trimmed of fat and cut in 1-in. cubes
Salt
Pepper
2 tbsp. Worcestershire sauce
1 bay leaf
½ cup dry white wine

Chill the consommé until the fat rises to the top, hardens, and can be lifted off; or skim off the fat by using a bulb-type baster. Drain canned vegetables reserving liquid.

Melt the margarine in a large nonstick skillet. Season the veal with salt and pepper and brown it in the melted margarine. Add the consommé, Worcestershire sauce, bay leaf, wine, and the liquid from

61

all the canned vegetables. Cover the skillet and simmer the mixture over very low heat for 1 hour or more until the meat is tender. Then uncover the pan and add the vegetables. Raise the heat to moderate and continue to simmer the mixture, uncovered, until nearly all of the liquid is evaporated.   *Makes 4 servings*

	Calories	Carbo-hydrate (gm)	Protein (gm)	Total Fat (gm)	Saturated Fat (gm)	Choles-terol (mg)
Total	1039.1	68.7	108.5	25.3	11.4	356.4
Per Serving	259.8	17.2	27.1	6.3	2.9	89.1

Low-Fat Veal Parmigiana

1½-lb. lean veal round (thinly sliced), trimmed of fat and cut in 6 pieces
¼ cup bread crumbs
1 tbsp. diet margarine
16-oz. can tomato sauce

2 tsp. Italian seasoning or oregano
1½ tsp. garlic salt
⅛ tsp. pepper
3 oz. part-skim mozzarella cheese, sliced

Dip the veal pieces in the bread crumbs until they are lightly coated. Melt the margarine in a large nonstick skillet. Add the coated veal and brown it slowly, turning once. Remove the veal from the skillet, and arrange it in a single layer in a shallow baking dish. Spoon the tomato sauce over the veal. Then season it with Italian seasoning, garlic salt, and pepper. Top the veal with the mozzarella slices. Bake uncovered in a preheated 350° oven for 20 to 25 minutes, until the cheese is melted and bubbly.   *Makes 6 servings*

	Calories	Carbo-hydrate (gm)	Protein (gm)	Total Fat (gm)	Saturated Fat (gm)	Choles-terol (mg)
Total	1411.3	52.9	190.7	55.1	20.3	535.3
Per Serving	235.2	8.8	31.8	9.2	3.4	89.2

---

gm = grams; mg = milligrams Nutritional figures are approximate. Figures are based on findings of U.S. Department of Agriculture.

Veal Piccata

1 tbsp. diet margarine
1½ lb. lean veal for
    scallopini, trimmed
    of fat and cut in 6
    pieces
1 envelope or cube
    chicken bouillon

½ cup dry white wine
¼ cup water
1 lemon
6 sprigs parsley

Melt the margarine in a large nonstick skillet. Add the veal and brown it quickly on both sides. Remove the veal to a platter. Stir the bouillon, wine, water, and juice of 1 lemon half into the skillet, scraping the pan to loosen the brown bits. Return the veal to the pan and cook it over high heat for about 5 minutes until it is tender. Return the veal to the serving platter and garnish it with slices of the remaining lemon and parsley sprigs.

Makes 6 servings

	Calories	Carbo-hydrate (gm)	Protein (gm)	Total Fat (gm)	Saturated Fat (gm)	Choles-terol (mg)
Total	1041.9	23.1	145.0	45.0	19.0	480.0
Per Serving	173.7	3.9	24.2	7.5	3.2	80.0

Skinny Schnitzel

2 tbsp. diet margarine
1½-lb. veal round steak,
    ¾-inch thick,
    trimmed of fat
1 envelope or 1 cube
    chicken or beef
    bouillon

½ cup boiling water
3 tbsp. lemon juice
½ tsp. butter-flavored
    salt
⅛ tsp. pepper
¼ cup chopped
    parsley

Melt the margarine over moderate heat in a large non-stick skillet. Add the veal and brown it on both sides. Dissolve the bouillon in ½ cup boiling water and add this to the skillet. At the same time, add the lemon juice, salt, and pepper. Cover the pan and bring the mixture to boiling. Lower the heat and simmer the meat for about 30 minutes until it is tender. Then stir in the

parsley. Remove the steak to a serving platter, and
pour the pan juices over it.   *Makes 6 servings*

	Calories	Carbohydrate (gm)	Protein (gm)	Total Fat (gm)	Saturated Fat (gm)	Cholesterol (mg)
Total	1008.4	3.8	137.2	44.0	18.0	483.0
Per Serving	168.0	0.6	22.9	7.3	3.0	80.5

Versatile Lamb

Once upon a time, lamb was seasonal meat available
mainly in the spring. Today lamb is here year-round for
a patio cookout or fireside supper.

Lamb is a lean and luscious main course for dieters.
It wears most of its fat on the outside, where it is easily
trimmable by the calorie-wise cook. Because lamb is
young and succulent, it doesn't need fatty marbling to
provide tenderness.

If you've served lamb well done and have been dis-
appointed in its taste or texture, next time try it Euro-
pean-style. Broil or sauté it so there's still a tinge of inner pinkness, or roast it to an internal temperature of
only about 165°. Lamb is rare at 165° to 170°, medium
at 174°, and well done at 180°.

Lamb is just as versatile as beef. Large tender cuts
like leg, sirloin, loin, rack, crown, and shoulder can be
oven roasted. And smaller cuts such as leg or sirloin
steaks, chops, and fat-trimmed ground patties can be
broiled, barbecued, or sautéed. (Steaks are the lowest
in calories.) The less tender, less expensive cuts of
lamb can be braised or simmered to scrumptious tenderness.

Recipes

Stir-Fried Lamb with Bean Sprouts

1 tbsp. diet margarine
1½ lb. lean boneless leg
    of lamb, trimmed of
    fat and cut in 1 x
    2½-in. strips
4 green onions, sliced

1½ tsp. crushed garlic
    cloves
2 tbsp. flour
2 tbsp. soy sauce
1½ lb. fresh bean
    sprouts, cooked
    and drained

Melt the diet margarine in a nonstick skillet. Add the lamb strips and brown them lightly. Then mix the onions and garlic with the meat and continue to cook for about 5 minutes, stirring constantly. Sprinkle the flour over this mixture, cooking and stirring until it is well blended with the lamb and onions. Add the soy sauce and continue cooking and stirring until the lamb is tender. Serve the meat mixture on a bed of bean sprouts. *Makes 6 servings*

	Calories	Carbo-hydrate (gm)	Protein (gm)	Total Fat (gm)	Saturated Fat (gm)	Choles-terol (mg)
Total	1580.8	55.8	218.2	54.1	29.8	681.6
Per Serving	263.5	9.3	36.4	9.0	5.0	113.6

Chinese Sweet 'n' Sour Lamb

1 lb. boneless lean leg
    of lamb, trimmed of
    fat and sliced thinly
    across the grain
Unseasoned meat
    tenderizer
2 onions
8½-oz. can water
    chestnuts
1 green pepper
2 firm, ripe tomatoes
2 tbsp. soy sauce

8-oz. can
    unsweetened
    pineapple
    chunks or
    tidbits, packed
    in juice
2 tbsp. catsup
1 tbsp. wine vinegar
1 tbsp. cornstarch
3 tbsp. cold water

Moisten the meat with water, and sprinkle it with meat tenderizer. Cut the onions into thin wedges; drain and slice the water chestnuts; cut the green pepper into 1½-inch squares; and cut the tomatoes into eighths.

Heat the soy sauce in a nonstick skillet. Add the lamb and brown it over high heat stirring rapidly until the liquid evaporates. Add the onion, water chestnuts, and green pepper, and continue stir-frying for about 3 minutes. Then add the undrained pineapple, catsup, and vinegar. Heat the contents of the skillet to boiling. In a cup, mix the cornstarch with the cold water until it is smooth. Add this mixture to the sauce in the skillet and continue heating, stirring constantly, until the sauce clears and thickens. Stir in tomato chunks.

Makes 6 servings

	Calories	Carbo-hydrate (gm)	Protein (gm)	Total Fat (gm)	Saturated Fat (gm)	Choles-terol (mg)
Total	1287.8	109.3	141.5	32.0	19.2	454.4
Per Serving	214.6	18.2	23.6	5.3	3.2	75.7

Herbed Lamb Chops

2 tbsp. flour
1 tsp. dry mustard
½ tsp. salt
¼ tsp. thyme
⅛ tsp. oregano
8 loin lamb chops, 1-in. thick, trimmed of fat

Mix the flour, mustard, salt, thyme, and oregano together in a paper bag. Add the lamb chops, a few at a time and shake the bag until they are coated with the flour mixture. Place the coated chops on a rack on a broiling pan placed 3 to 4 inches from the heat source. Broil about 7 minutes on each side, or until the desired doneness is reached.

Makes 8 servings

	Calories	Carbo-hydrate (gm)	Protein (gm)	Total Fat (gm)	Saturated Fat (gm)	Choles-terol (mg)
Total	3259.2	12.4	201.7	264.1	144.0	1072.0
Per Serving	407.4	1.6	25.2	33.0	18.0	134.0

gm = grams; mg = milligrams. Nutritional figures are approximate. Figures are based on findings of U.S. Department of Agriculture.

Lamb and Artichokes en Brochette

2 pkg. (9 oz. each)
　　frozen artichoke
　　hearts
1/2 cup low-calorie
　　French salad
　　dressing
1/4 cup fresh lemon juice

2 tsp. salt
1 tsp. marjoram or
　　oregano leaves
1/4 tsp. pepper
1 1/2 lb. lean boneless
　　leg of lamb,
　　trimmed of fat
　　and cut in 1 1/2-in.
　　cubes
2 large tomatoes

Cook the artichokes according to the package directions, drain and allow to cool. In a large bowl mix together the French dressing, lemon juice, and seasonings. Add the lamb and artichokes and mix lightly. Cover the bowl and refrigerate for several hours or overnight.

Place the lamb on skewers. Cut each of the tomatoes into 6 wedges and alternate the artichokes and tomatoes on another set of skewers. Brush the lamb and vegetables with the marinade. Broil the lamb 3 to 5 inches from the heat source for 5 to 7 minutes on each side, or until they have reached the desired doneness. Broil the artichoke kebabs for 3 to 4 minutes on each side.　　　*Makes 6 servings*

	Calories	Carbo-hydrate (gm)	Protein (gm)	Total Fat (gm)	Saturated Fat (gm)	Cholesterol (mg)
Total	1484.6	74.4	211.7	48.0	28.8	681.6
Per Serving	247.4	12.4	35.3	8.0	4.8	113.6

Baked Lamb Chops with Rice

8 lamb shoulder chops,
　　1-in. thick, trimmed
　　of fat
1 cup uncooked rice
2 medium onions,
　　sliced

2 medium green
　　peppers, sliced
16-oz. can tomatoes
10 1/2-oz. can beef
　　bouillon or broth

Place the lamb chops under the broiler until they are just brown. Place the rice in a baking dish. Then cover the rice with chops, onion, green pepper, and tomatoes. Pour the bouillon over all. Cover the baking dish, and bake the meat and vegetables in a preheated 350° oven for 1½ hours.   *Makes 8 servings*

	Calories	Carbo-hydrate (gm)	Protein (gm)	Total Fat (gm)	Saturated Fat (gm)	Choles-terol (mg)
Total	4159.2	204.9	235.2	267.0	144.0	1135.4
Per Serving	519.9	25.6	29.4	33.4	18.0	141.9

Skinny Skewered Lamb

2 green peppers
3 large carrots
4 celery stalks
½ lb. fresh mushrooms
1½ lb. lean boneless leg
of lamb, trimmed of
fat and cut in ¾-in.
cubes

1½ tsp. salt
Dash black pepper
3 cups tomato sauce
¾ tsp. whole cloves
Dash oregano
2 tbsp. Worces-
tershire sauce

Add water to a large skillet to a ½-inch depth. Cut the green peppers, carrots and celery, into 1-inch chunks; add them to skillet with the mushrooms. Cover and simmer 10 minutes. Drain well. Arrange the meat and vegetables on 6 skewers and place the skewers in a single layer in a roasting pan. Sprinkle the meat and vegetables with salt and pepper. In a separate bowl, combine the tomato sauce, cloves, oregano, and Worcestershire sauce. Pour this mixture over the kebabs. Bake in a preheated 325° oven for 30 to 45 minutes — or until the lamb is tender — basting frequently with the pan liquid.   *Makes 6 servings*

	Calories	Carbo-hydrate (gm)	Protein (gm)	Total Fat (gm)	Saturated Fat (gm)	Choles-terol (mg)
Total	1762.0	112.3	224.7	51.7	28.8	681.6
Per Serving	293.6	18.7	37.5	8.6	4.8	113.6

gm = grams; mg = milligrams. Nutritional figures are approximate. Figures are based on findings of U.S. Department of Agriculture

Slim Pork and Ham

Once upon a time, pork was plenty pudgy, but thanks to modern breeding techniques, today's pork contains only half as much fat as in the olden days and far fewer calories. Although not as trim as veal, pork does beat out many cuts of beef in the calorie sweepstakes. Another point in pork's favor: it's always served well done, which eliminates even more fat. Comparable cuts of beef that have been broiled or roasted are generally served rare.

Which brings us to another point about pork. Many homemakers, aware that pork must be cooked through, habitually overcook it and thereby ruin its delightful taste and texture. Many old cookbooks and meat thermometers suggest an internal temperature of 185°, but research shows that pork is more tender and tasty when served at 170°, which is perfectly safe, since all trichinae are killed at 140°. When cooking pork, a meat thermometer is doubly important to avoid either undercooking or overcooking.

Much of the cured ham available in supermarkets is "fully cooked" or "ready to eat," which means that it needs only sufficient cooking to warm it through and improve its flavor. Such meat should always be properly identified on the can, label, or wrapper. Reheat ready-to-eat whole or half hams to an internal temperature of 130° in a preheated 300° or 325° oven for the best flavor. Ready-to-eat ham slices can be sautéed in a nonstick skillet or barbecued or broiled until heated through.

Cured or smoked pork that is labeled "cook before eating" must, of course, be cooked. Follow the label directions. Or, roast an uncooked ham to an internal temperature of 160° in a preheated 300° or 325° oven. Uncooked picnic roast (shoulder) or boneless butt (cottage roll) should be roasted to 170° or simmered in liquid until tender.

Even though modern breeding techniques result in leaner stock, some cuts of pork are still exceedingly high in fat and calories. These should be avoided by the committed calorie-counter. Included are bacon (69 percent fat and 3,016 calories per pound), sausage (50 percent fat and 2,259 calories per pound), and spareribs (33 percent fat and 1,637 calories per pound). If you crave these diet crashers, try some substitutions. Canadian bacon (only 980 calories per pound) can be sliced and served in place of fatty bacon, and homemade sausage patties can be prepared from lean ground pork. Veal or lamb ribs cut from the breast make an interesting stand-in for fatty pork spareribs.

Recipes

Pork Steak Viennese

1-lb. lean pork leg steak
(or fresh ham slice)
trimmed of fat
1½ tsp. salt
½ tsp. pepper
1-lb. 11-oz. can
sauerkraut, drained

1-lb. can whole
tomatoes,
undrained
2½ tbsp. instant onion
1 green pepper, cut
in 1-in. strips
¼ tsp. thyme

Spray a nonstick skillet with vegetable coating for no-fat frying and brown the meat slowly. Season the browned meat on both sides with the salt and ¼ teaspoon of pepper. In a bowl, combine the other ¼ teaspoon of pepper with the sauerkraut, tomatoes, onion, green pepper, and thyme. Mix well and pour into 7½ x 11¾-inch baking dish. Place the meat on top of the mixture. Cover with aluminum foil and bake 30 minutes in a preheated 325° oven. Then uncover and bake another 30 minutes — or until the pork is tender.

Makes 4 servings

	Calories	Carbo-hydrate (gm)	Protein (gm)	Total Fat (gm)	Saturated Fat (gm)	Choles-terol (mg)
Total	1556.0	52.0	106.4	103.4	37.3	405.1
Per Serving	389.0	13.0	26.6	25.9	9.3	101.3

Ham Patties Aloha

1½ -lb. cooked smoked
ham, trimmed of fat
and ground
1 tsp. grated onion
1 tbsp. chopped parsley
1 tbsp. prepared
mustard

1 egg, beaten
8 pineapple slices
(unsweetened,
juice-packed)
drained
reserving 2 tbsp.
juice
8 tbsp. crushed
cornflakes

Mix the ham with the onion, parsley, mustard, egg, and the 2 tablespoons pineapple juice. Shape the meat into 8 patties and roll in the crushed cornflakes. Arrange the pineapple slices in a shallow baking dish. Place 1 patty on each pineapple slice. Bake in a preheated 375° oven for 25 to 30 minutes. *Makes 8 servings*

	Calories	Carbo-hydrate (gm)	Protein (gm)	Total Fat (gm)	Saturated Fat (gm)	Choles-terol (mg)
Total	2390.5	107.6	151.0	158.0	58.0	860.0
Per Serving	298.8	13.5	18.9	19.8	7.3	107.5

Pineapple-Ham Stir Fry

1 tbsp. diet margarine
1½ lb. lean cooked
    smoked ham,
    trimmed of fat and
    cut in 1-in. strips
2 large onions, sliced
2 large green peppers,
    sliced

2 cups unsweetened
    pineapple
    chunks, juice
    packed
2 tbsp. cornstarch
¾ tsp. salt
¼ tsp. pepper
1 tbsp. soy sauce

Melt the margarine in a large, nonstick skillet. Add the ham, onions, and green peppers, and sauté over moderate heat until the ham is browned. Drain the pineapple, reserving the juice. Add enough water to the juice to make ¾ of a cup of liquid. Combine the cornstarch, salt, pepper, soy sauce, and pineapple liquid in a bowl. Add this to the ham and vegetables, and continue cooking over low heat, stirring constantly, until the sauce has thickened. Add pineapple chunks.

Makes 6 servings

	Calories	Carbo-hydrate (gm)	Protein (gm)	Total Fat (gm)	Saturated Fat (gm)	Choles-terol (mg)
Total	1954.7	119.3	217.0	70.0	25.0	600.0
Per Serving	325.8	19.9	36.2	11.7	4.2	100.0

gm = grams; mg = milligrams. Nutritional figures are approximate. Figures are based on findings of U.S. Department of Agriculture.

Chinese Pork

1½-lb. lean boneless pork
   shoulder,
   trimmed of fat and
   cut in 1-in. cubes
2 beef bouillon cubes
1 cup hot water
11-oz. can unsweetened
   juice-packed
   mandarin oranges,
   drained reserving
   juice
¼ cup soy sauce
1 tbsp. instant minced
   onion
½ tsp. ground ginger

2 tbsp. cornstarch
¼ cup cold water
4-oz. can water
   chestnuts,
   drained and
   sliced
2 green peppers, in
   ¼-in. strips
1 cup sliced
   mushrooms
1 cup sliced celery
   cabbage (cut
   diagonally ½- to
   ¾- in. thick)

Spray a non-stick skillet with vegetable coating for no-fat frying. Add the meat and brown slowly. Dissolve the bouillon cubes in 1 cup hot water. Add this with the liquid from the oranges, the soy sauce, minced onion, and ginger to the pork. Bring the mixture to a boil; then cover, reduce the heat, and simmer about 30 minutes. In a separate bowl, blend cornstarch with ¼ cup cold water. Gradually add the cornstarch mixture to the meat, cooking and stirring constantly until the sauce is thick and clear. Then add the water chestnuts, green pepper, mushrooms, and celery cabbage. Cover and continue to cook over low heat 7 minutes. Fold in the mandarin oranges just before serving.

Makes 8 servings

	Calories	Carbo-hydrate (gm)	Protein (gm)	Total Fat (gm)	Saturated Fat (gm)	Choles-terol (mg)
Total	1714.1	80.7	219.0	49.3	24.0	606.0
Per Serving	214.3	10.1	27.3	6.2	3.0	75.8

---

gm = grams; mg = milligrams. Nutritional figures are approximate
Figures are based on findings of U.S. Department of Agriculture.

Ground Meat Favorites

Hamburger is one of America's favorite meats. The typical American eats in excess of 50 pounds of ground meat a year, much of it, unfortunately, calorie-contaminated with excess fat. Most prepackaged ground meat contains close to the legal limit of fat — 30 percent — and weighs in at more than 1600 calories per pound. Fat-trimmed beef, by contrast, is less than 700 calories per pound. You can eliminate more than 50,000 excess calories this year by switching from prepackaged hamburger to fat-trimmed beef that has been custom-ground to your order. Simply pick out a piece of lean bottom round and ask the butcher to trim away the fat and grind the lean to order. Almost all supermarkets will perform this service for you, especially when you explain that you have to eliminate as much fat as possible from your diet. Rest assured that you won't be the first customer to request custom-ground, fat-trimmed beef. Many heart-smart cholesterol watchers shop for it as a matter of prudence.

Isn't lean hamburger more expensive? The price tag for boneless bottom round is generally at least one-third higher than ready-ground hamburger. But the price difference is really not as great as it appears. Lean hamburger won't shrink the way fatty hamburger will, so one pound will give you four servings, instead of three or less. And the nutritive value is much higher, because the fat in the packaged ground meat is replaced with protein in the lean meat. Here's how fatty hamburger and lean ground compare:

1 Pound, Raw	Fat	Protein	Calories
Hamburger, 29% fat	148 grams	73 grams	1,647
Lean ground round, trimmed of fat	21 grams	98 grams	612

Isn't lean hamburger dry? Only if you overcook it. Like all lean meat, fat-trimmed hamburger can't stand up to blast-furnace temperatures and prolonged cooking times. The best way to broil lean burgers is to mix the meat with crushed ice, season it, and broil it only until it is well browned on the outside. The inside should remain pink and juicy.

You can do anything with lean hamburger that you can do with fatty hamburger. Meat loaf and casserole dishes are particularly well suited to lean meat since a casserole dish made with fatty hamburger will be greasy and undigestible (as well as fattening) because the fat has nowhere to escape. Meat loaf made with lean meat is delicious hot or cold, while fatty meat loaf is unpleasantly greasy when chilled.

Other Ground Meats

Any meat can be fat-trimmed and ground to order. Try pork, lamb, or veal for a change. If you're fortunate enough to live in an area where the stores stock and sell raw ground turkeyburger, be sure to take advantage of this nonfattening treat — only 736 calories a pound! If freshly ground turkey is unavailable, buy large frozen turkey thighs. Defrost them, remove the meat from the bones (discarding the skin) and put the meat through a grinder. Three large thighs equals about 2 pounds of ground meat.

Recipes

Chopped Steak Suey

2 lb. lean ground round steak
1 onion, cut in eighths
2 beef bouillon cubes
1/2 cup hot water
4-oz. can whole mushrooms, drained reserving liquid
1/3 cup soy sauce

2 tbsp. cornstarch
5- to 6 1/2-oz. can water chestnuts, drained and halved
16-oz. can bean sprouts, drained
16-oz. can Chinese vegetables, drained
1/4 cup pimiento strips

Brown the ground meat in a large nonstick skillet. Do not add any oil to the pan because the meat will release enough of its own fat. Add the onion to the browned meat and continue to cook over low heat for 5 minutes. Before going any further, pour off all the fat that has accumulated in the pan. Dissolve bouillon cubes in hot water. Then combine the liquid from the mushrooms with the bouillon and add this to the meat along with the soy sauce and cornstarch. Bring the liquid to a boil, then reduce the heat and simmer, stirring constantly, until the mixture thickens. Stir in the mushrooms, water chestnuts, bean sprouts, and Chinese vegetables, cooking just until they are heated through. Stir in the pimiento strips just before serving.

Makes 8 servings

	Calories	Carbohydrate (gm)	Protein (gm)	Total Fat (gm)	Saturated Fat (gm)	Cholesterol (mg)
Total	1964.4	95.4	312.9	36.1	11.9	847.4
Per Serving	245.6	11.9	39.1	4.5	1.5	105.9

gm = grams; mg = milligrams. Nutritional figures are approximate. Figures are based on findings of U.S. Department of Agriculture.

Meat Loaf for Diet Watchers

2 lb. lean ground round
  steak
2 tsp. salt or garlic salt
¼ tsp. pepper
2 eggs

½ cup high-protein
  cereal,
  unsweetened
½ cup skim milk
¼ cup chopped
  onion
¼ tsp. dried sage

Mix all of the ingredients together thoroughly and form the meat into a loaf in a shallow baking pan. Bake in a preheated 350° oven for about 1 hour, basting occasionally with juices. *Makes 8 servings*

Diet hint: The calorie-wise cook can save a whopping 100 calories (that's 12½ per serving) by using 4 egg whites instead of 2 whole eggs. Egg whites have hardly a trace of saturated fat or cholesterol.

	Calories	Carbo-hydrate (gm)	Protein (gm)	Total Fat (gm)	Saturated Fat (gm)	Choles-terol (mg)
Total	1739.9	16.8	303.7	47.7	15.9	1347.9
Per Serving	217.5	2.1	38.0	6.0	2.0	168.5

Succulent Burgers

2 lb. lean ground round
  steak
2 tbsp. snipped chives

¼ cup crushed ice
1 tsp. bitters

Combine all the ingredients and mix well. Shape into 8 patties and place them on a rack in the broiler, 4 inches from the heat source. Broil about 10 minutes, turning once. *Makes 8 servings*

	Calories	Carbo-hydrate (gm)	Protein (gm)	Total Fat (gm)	Saturated Fat (gm)	Choles-terol (mg)
Total	1488.3	1.5	284.4	35.6	11.9	841.4
Per Serving	186.0	0.2	35.6	4.5	1.5	105.2

Turkey Sloppy Joes

1 tbsp. diet margarine
1 lb. fresh ground
  turkey
1½ cups chopped onion
1½ cups chopped celery
½ cup chopped green
  pepper

10½-oz. can condensed
  tomato soup
1 tsp. salt
Dash of pepper
12 toasted buns

Melt the margarine in a large nonstick skillet. Add the ground turkey and cook over low heat until browned. Then add the chopped vegetables and continue to cook until they are tender. Stir in the soup, salt, and pepper, cover and simmer for about 30 minutes. Serve on toasted buns.   *Makes 12 servings*

	Calories	Carbohydrate (gm)	Protein (gm)	Total Fat (gm)	Saturated Fat (gm)	Cholesterol (mg)
Total	2684.1	320.0	190.9	65.2	22.1	430.7
Per Serving	223.7	26.7	15.9	5.4	1.8	35.9

Turkey Chili

1 tbsp. diet margarine
1¼ lb. fresh ground
  turkey
1 cup chopped onion
½ cup chopped green
  pepper
½ cup chopped red
  pepper

16-oz. can chopped
  tomatoes,
  undrained
2 tsp. salt
1 tsp. chili powder
½ tsp. black pepper
¼ tsp. red pepper

Melt the margarine in a heavy nonstick skillet. Add the turkey, onion, and peppers, and brown them slowly. Then add the tomatoes (with the juice) and the seasonings. Cover and simmer the mixture for about 15 minutes.   *Makes 6 servings*

	Calories	Carbohydrate (gm)	Protein (gm)	Total Fat (gm)	Saturated Fat (gm)	Cholesterol (mg)
Total	1293.9	34.5	189.7	42.3	13.4	508.2
Per Serving	215.6	5.8	31.6	7.1	2.2	84.7

Chicken and Turkey

Of all the main course choices available to dieters, chicken is the unchallenged champion in terms of popularity, availability, versatility, and affordability. Chicken is lower in calories than any other meat. It's also cholesterol-wise because of its relative lack of saturated fat.

The popularity of chicken and its congenial calorie count are due to modern farming methods that make young spring chickens the least expensive and most available. These prize broiler-fryer chickens are also the prime choice nutritionally.

How to Cook a Chicken

Broiling. Because of the fat in chicken skin, broiler-fryer chickens can be broiled without additional fat.

1. Sprinkle the chicken halves, quarters, or pieces with salt, pepper, lemon juice, and an herb such as tar-

ragon, thyme, or basil.

2. Place the pieces skin side down on a broiler rack. In the broiler of a gas range, the chicken should be 3 to 6 inches from the heat source; in an electric range, the distance should be 6 to 9 inches.

3. Broil the chicken for 20 to 25 minutes. Then turn it and broil 15 to 20 minutes longer.

4. If you like, you can baste the chicken with barbecue sauce near the end of the cooking time.

Frying. One of the most popular ways to cook chicken is to fry it. It's also the most fattening way. What makes frying so fattening, of course, is the oil used in the frying process. So a simple way of decalorizing fried chicken is to eliminate the oil.

1. Cut a broiler-fryer chicken into serving pieces — or buy one that is already cut up. A 2-pound chicken will serve 4 people.

2. In a paper bag, mix 3 tablespoons flour with 1 teaspoon salt, ½ teaspoon pepper, and 1 teaspoon paprika.

3. Add the chicken, a few pieces at a time, to the bag, and shake them until the chicken is coated.

4. Place the chicken in a nonstick baking dish, skin side down.

5. Bake the chicken for about 25 minutes at 400°.

6. Turn the chicken over and bake 20 to 25 minutes more, until it is tender, brown and crisp.

7. Before serving, blot the chicken with paper toweling.

Simmering. Chicken simmered in water and seasonings makes a great beginning for other dishes.

1. Use a broiler-fryer chicken, whole or cut into serving pieces.

2. Put the chicken in a kettle and add 2 cups of water, 1 small sliced onion, 3 celery tops, 1 teaspoon salt and ½ teaspoon pepper.

3. Bring the water to a boil.

4. Cover the kettle, reduce the heat, and simmer the chicken for about 1 hour until it's tender.

5. Strain the broth

6. Refrigerate the chicken and broth in separate containers.

7. When the chicken is cool, remove the meat from

the skin and bones, and cut it into chunks.

8. Skim the fat from the surface of the broth.

Roasting. Another healthy and low-calorie way of preparing chicken is roasting it. In this dry-heat method, the chicken is cooked to juicy tenderness while the bird's excess fat is melted away.

1. Even though it may seem more appropriate to use a roasting chicken, buy a broiler-fryer. It is lower in calories and faster to cook.

2. Sprinkle the neck and body cavities with 1 teaspoon salt.

3. If you like, stuff the body cavity with your favorite stuffing.

4. Hook the wing tips onto the chicken's back to hold the neck skin. Tie the legs together, then tie them to the tail.

5. Place the chicken in a shallow roasting pan. Do not brush the chicken with fat.

6. Roast the chicken according to the following timetable.

Weight	Time per Pound	Temperature	Approx. Amt. Stuffing	Approx. Total Time*
1½ lb.	40 min.	400°	¾ cup	1 hour
2 lb.	35 min.	400°	1 cup	1 hr. 10 min.
2½ lb.	30 min.	375°	1¼ cups	1 hr. 15 min.
3 lb.	30 min.	375°	1½ cups	1 hr. 30 min.
3½ lb.	30 min.	375°	1¾ cups	1 hr. 45 min.
4 lb.	30 min.	375°	2 cups	2 hours
4½ lb.	30 min.	375°	2¼ cups	2 hrs. 15 min.
5 lb.	30 min.	375°	2½ cups	2 hrs. 30 min.

*If the chicken is stuffed, add 15 min. to the total roasting time.

7. When the chicken is done, the drumstick meat will feel soft when pressed between your fingers, and the leg will twist easily out of the thigh joint. Another way of testing the chicken for doneness is to pierce the skin of the breast with a fork. If the liquid that seeps out is clear, not yellow, the chicken is done.

8. Let the chicken stand about 10 minutes before carving.

Baked Chicken with Mushrooms

2 (2 lb. each) broiler-
 fryer chickens,
 quartered
1½ tsp. salt
1 tsp. celery seed

½ tsp. dried
 marjoram
8-oz. can
 mushrooms,
 drained
 reserving liquid

Sprinkle the chicken quarters with salt and place skin side up in a shallow baking dish. Season them with celery seed and marjoram. Add the liquid from the mushrooms and bake the chicken in a preheated 350° oven for 30 minutes, occasionally spooning the liquid over the meat. Then add the mushrooms to the pan and continue baking 20 or 30 minutes longer until the chicken is tender. Drain the liquid from the pan. Using a bulb-type baster, skim the fat from the liquid so the liquid can be used as a gravy.   *Makes 8 servings*

	Calories	Carbo-hydrate (gm)	Protein (gm)	Total Fat (gm)	Saturated Fat (gm)	Choles-terol (mg)
Total	1767.5	6.0	265.5	68.6	27.4	1110.5
Per Serving	220.9	0.8	33.2	8.6	3.4	138.8

Chicken Mediterranean

1 tbsp. grated lemon
 peel
½ cup water
¼ cup lemon juice
1 tsp. thyme
1 tsp. garlic salt

½ tsp. black pepper
2-lb. broiler-fryer
 chicken,
 quartered
1 lemon, sliced
¼ cup chopped
 parsley

Combine the grated lemon peel, water, lemon juice, thyme, garlic salt, and pepper. Spoon this mixture over the chicken, coating it well. Refrigerate 3 to 4 hours, turning chicken in the marinade several times.

Arrange the chicken in a single layer in a shallow baking dish. Save the marinade. Bake the chicken, uncovered, in a preheated 425° oven for 25 minutes. Pour off the fat that accumulates in the pan. Lower the heat to 350°. Brush the chicken with the reserved marinade and bake for an additional 25 to 35 minutes until tender and brown. Garnish with lemon slices and parsley.

Makes 4 servings

	Calories	Carbo-hydrate (gm)	Protein (gm)	Total Fat (gm)	Saturated Fat (gm)	Choles-terol (mg)
Total	886.6	5.8	130.7	34.3	13.7	555.7
Per Serving	221.7	1.5	32.7	8.6	3.4	138.9

Chicken Cacciatore

2 lb. broiler-fryer
    chicken pieces
2 tsp. salt
¼ tsp. pepper
1 tbsp. parsley

1 tsp. oregano
1 tsp. garlic salt
4 cups canned
    tomatoes

Place the chicken in a nonstick skillet. Beginning with skin side down, brown the chicken over medium heat about 15 minutes on each side. Do not add oil to the pan; the chicken will release enough of its own fat for frying. When the chicken is brown, add the remaining ingredients to the pan. Cover and simmer about 30 minutes until the chicken is tender. *Makes 4 servings*

	Calories	Carbo-hydrate (gm)	Protein (gm)	Total Fat (gm)	Saturated Fat (gm)	Choles-terol (mg)
Total	1065.4	40.0	138.3	38.3	13.7	555.7
Per Serving	266.4	10.0	34.6	9.6	3.4	138.9

---

gm = grams; mg = milligrams. Nutritional figures are approximate. Figures are based on findings of U.S. Department of Agriculture.

Chicken Pizza

2 lbs. chicken breasts,
   boned and skinned
   (2¹/₂ lbs. with bone
   will yield 2 lbs.
   boned)
1 tsp. onion salt
¹/₂ tsp. pepper
8 oz. can tomato sauce

4 oz. can
   mushrooms,
   undrained
¹/₂ tsp. oregano
1 cup shredded part-
   skim mozzarella
   cheese (4 oz.)

Season the chicken breasts with the onion salt and
pepper, and arrange them in a shallow baking dish.
Combine the tomato sauce, mushrooms, liquid, and
oregano in a bowl; then pour this over the chicken.
Bake the chicken, uncovered at 350° for 35 minutes or
more until it is tender. Sprinkle the cheese over the top
of the chicken, and return it to the oven for about 5
minutes, until the cheese is melted and bubbly.

Makes 8 servings

	Calories	Carbo-hydrate (gm)	Protein (gm)	Total Fat (gm)	Saturated Fat (gm)	Choles-terol (mg)
Total	1625.4	18.6	278.9	52.4	14.7	786.2
Per Serving	203.2	2.3	34.9	6.6	1.8	98.3

Chicken Kiev

4 whole chicken
   breasts (about 1 lb.
   each), boned,
   skinned, halved
1 tbsp. freeze-dried
   chives
1 tsp. butter-flavored
   salt
¹/₂ tsp. thyme

¹/₂ tsp. marjoram
¹/₄ tsp. ground black
   pepper
4 oz. Neufchatel
   cheese, cut in 8
   slices
2 eggs
2 tbsp. safflower oil
8 tbsp. seasoned
   bread crumbs

Pound the chicken breasts halves with a rolling pin until they are about ¹/₄ inch thick. Sprinkle with the chives

and seasonings. Place 1 cheese slice on the edge of each piece of chicken and roll up tightly, tucking in the sides to enclose the cheese completely. Secure the rolls with toothpicks. Beat the eggs with the oil in a shallow dish. Place the bread crumbs in another shallow dish. Dip the chicken rolls in the egg mixture, and then roll in the bread crumbs. Arrange the chicken in a single layer in a baking pan. Bake in a preheated oven at 450° for 20 minutes. *Makes 8 servings*

	Calories	Carbo-hydrate (gm)	Protein (gm)	Total Fat (gm)	Saturated Fat (gm)	Choles-terol (mg)
Total	2381.2	41.3	311.1	102.0	40.3	1496.8
Per Serving	297.7	5.2	38.9	12.8	5.0	187.1

Oven-Fried Chicken

1 cup crushed high-
  protein cereal,
  unsweetened
2 tsp. salt
1/4 tsp. pepper

2 lb. broiler-fryer
  chicken pieces
1/2 cup evaporated
  skim milk

Mix the crushed cereal, salt, and pepper together on a flat plate. Dip the chicken pieces into the milk, and then roll them in the cereal mixture. Place them, skin side down, on a nonstick cookie sheet and bake 30 minutes in a preheated 350° oven. Turn and bake on the other side for another 30 minutes.

Makes 4 servings

	Calories	Carbo-hydrate (gm)	Protein (gm)	Total Fat (gm)	Saturated Fat (gm)	Choles-terol (mg)
Total	1124.1	28.6	143.9	44.5	19.2	594.7
Per Serving	281.0	7.2	36.0	11.1	4.8	148.7

---

gm = grams; mg = milligrams. Nutritional figures are approximate. Figures are based on findings of U.S. Department of Agriculture.

Skinny Fried Chicken

2 lb. broiler-fryer
chicken pieces

2 tsp. salt
1/4 tsp. pepper

Place the chicken pieces in a large nonstick skillet. Do not add shortening or oil to the pan. Season the chicken with salt and pepper. Fry, uncovered, over moderate heat for 20 to 30 minutes. Turn the chicken over, season it again, and continue frying 20 or 30 minutes until tender.   *Makes 4 servings*

	Calories	Carbohydrate (gm)	Protein (gm)	Total Fat (gm)	Saturated Fat (gm)	Cholesterol (mg)
Total	864.4	0.0	130.3	34.3	13.7	555.7
Per Serving	216.1	0.0	32.6	8.6	3.4	138.9

Herbed Chicken

1 tsp. salt
3 tbsp. lemon juice
2 tbsp. water
1 tsp. rosemary
1 tsp. thyme

2 tsp. dried tarragon
leaves
1-lb. broiler-fryer
chicken, split in
half lengthwise

Make a basting sauce by combining all the ingredients except the chicken. Place the chicken on a broiler rack, skin side up, and brush it with the basting sauce. Broil the chicken 8 to 10 inches from the heat source for approximately 45 minutes, until tender, basting it as needed.   *Makes 4 servings*

	Calories	Carbohydrate (gm)	Protein (gm)	Total Fat (gm)	Saturated Fat (gm)	Cholesterol (mg)
Total	857.8	3.8	130.5	34.3	13.7	555.7
Per Serving	219.0	1.0	32.6	8.6	3.4	138.9

gm = grams; mg = milligrams. Nutritional figures are approximate. Figures are based on findings of U.S. Department of Agriculture.

Chicken with Vegetables

2 lb. broiler-fryer
  chicken pieces
1 bunch green onions,
  trimmed
2 cups water
1 tsp. salt
1/8 tsp. pepper

1 cup chopped
  asparagus
8-oz. can baby
  carrots, drained
4-oz. can sliced
  mushrooms,
  drained
3 tbsp. cornstarch
1/2 cup dry white wine

Brown the chicken pieces skin side down in a large, heavy nonstick skillet. Do not add oil to the skillet; the chicken will release enough of its own fat for frying. Drain off the fat that accumulates in the pan. Add the green onions, water, salt and pepper to the pan; cover and simmer the chicken about 45 minutes until tender. Before going any further, skim the fat from the pan using a bulb-type baster. Then add the asparagus, carrots, and mushrooms. Cover the pan, and simmer 10 minutes longer. Add the cornstarch to a little of the wine in a cup and blend well. Then add the rest of the wine. Stir the wine mixture into the skillet, and continue simmering, stirring occasionally, until the gravy is thickened and clear. *Makes 4 servings*

	Calories	Carbo-hydrate (gm)	Protein (gm)	Total Fat (gm)	Saturated Fat (gm)	Choles-terol (mg)
Total	1201.3	57.9	141.8	34.3	13.7	555.7
Per Serving	300.3	14.5	35.5	8.6	3.4	138.9

Chicken in Pouches

4 whole chicken
  breasts
2 thin slices of boiled
  ham
1 tbsp. soy sauce
2 tbsp. sherry

1 tbsp. chopped
  green onion
1 tsp. cornstarch
1/4 tsp. ground ginger
1/4 tsp. garlic powder

Bone and skin the chicken breasts. Slice each breast diagonally into 3 long pieces. Trim the fat from the ham and cut each slice into 3 portions. Combine the soy sauce, sherry, onion, cornstarch, ginger, and garlic powder in a bowl. Pour this mixture over the chicken and ham and let it stand at room temperature, uncovered, for 30 minutes or longer.

Cut 6 rectangles of aluminum foil, about 6 x 12 inches. Place a portion of ham on each piece of foil. On top of the ham place 2 pieces of chicken side by side. Spoon any remaining marinade over the meat. Fold the foil over to make square pouches, using a double fold at the edges. Place the pouches on a baking sheet and bake in a preheated 400° oven for 20 minutes. Serve in the pouches.   *Makes 6 servings*

	Calories	Carbo-hydrate (gm)	Protein (gm)	Total Fat (gm)	Saturated Fat (gm)	Choles-terol (mg)
Total	913.6	9.1	155.1	24.0	11.0	483.0
Per Serving	152.3	1.5	25.9	4.0	1.8	80.5

Gala Chicken

2-lb. broiler-fryer chicken, halved
1 tsp. salt

¼ cup unsweetened apple juice
¼ cup dry white wine

Place the chicken skin side down on a broiler rack and season it with half the salt. Combine the apple juice and wine and pour half the mixture into the cavities of the chicken. Broil the chicken about 10 inches from the heat source about 30 minutes. Then turn the chicken over, season it with the rest of the salt, and brush it with the remaining wine mixture. Broil it 30 minutes longer until it is tender.   *Makes 4 servings*

	Calories	Carbo-hydrate (gm)	Protein (gm)	Total Fat (gm)	Saturated Fat (gm)	Choles-terol (mg)
Total	942.9	9.8	130.3	34.3	13.7	555.7
Per Serving	235.7	2.5	32.6	8.6	3.4	138.9

gm = grams; mg = milligrams. Nutritional figures are approximate. Figures are based on findings of U.S. Department of Agriculture.

French Turkey Ragout

1¼ lb. turkey thighs
2 tbsp. water
2 cups water
2 medium white potatoes, peeled and halved
1 cup tomato juice
2 onions, chopped

1 garlic clove, minced
1 bay leaf
1 lb. small carrots, fresh or frozen
½ tsp. salt
¼ tsp. pepper
2 tbsp. flour
¼ cup cold water

With a sharp knife, strip the turkey meat from the bone, and cut it into 1½-inch cubes. Put the turkey, skin side down, in a heavy nonstick Dutch oven and add 2 tablespoons water. Cover and cook over high heat until the water evaporates and the turkey cubes begin to brown in their own melted fat. Then lower the heat, uncover the pot, and continue to cook the turkey until it is brown on all sides. Before going any further, drain the accumulated fat from the pot. Then add 2 cups water and all the remaining ingredients, except the flour and ¼ cup water. Cover the pot and simmer the contents over low heat for 35 to 45 minutes — until the turkey is tender. Then combine the flour with ¼ cup cold water and stir this mixture into the pot. Continue to cook and stir until the gravy has thickened. *Makes 4 servings*

	Calories	Carbo-hydrate (gm)	Protein (gm)	Total Fat (gm)	Saturated Fat (gm)	Choles-terol (mg)
Total	1407.3	112.4	155.7	36.7	13.7	461.6
Per Serving	351.8	28.1	38.9	9.2	3.4	115.4

Turkey Marengo

3 lb. turkey wings, tips removed
1 cup sliced onions
4-oz. can sliced mushrooms, undrained

1-lb. can tomatoes
½ cup dry white wine
2 cups water
1 tsp. salt
½ tsp. pepper
1 tsp. oregano

Separate the wing sections and place in a nonstick Dutch oven. Brown them without adding any oil to the pot. After the turkey has browned, add all of the remaining ingredients. Cover the pot and simmer over low heat for 2 hours. Refrigerate until serving time.

Just before serving, remove the pot from the refrigerator. The fat will have floated to the top and congealed. Lift off the fat and discard it. Then reheat the turkey, uncovered, simmering it for 10 or 15 minutes, until most of the liquid has evaporated.

Makes 6 servings

	Calories	Carbo-hydrate (gm)	Protein (gm)	Total Fat (gm)	Saturated Fat (gm)	Choles-terol (mg)
Total	2059.8	37.6	193.6	111.7	27.4	719.8
Per Serving	343.2	6.3	32.3	18.6	4.6	120.0

Apple-Bacon Poultry Stuffing

6 apples, peeled and chopped
2 cups cubed protein bread, lightly toasted
1/2 cup chopped onion
1/2 cup cubed Canadian bacon
1 cup minced celery
1/4 cup chopped parsley
1 tsp. salt
1/4 tsp. pepper
1 tsp. poultry seasoning
1/2 cup hot giblet stock or boiling water

Combine all the ingredients, mixing them lightly. Loosely fill the cavity of a turkey, chicken, or rock Cornish hen. The stuffing can also be baked in a 1 1/2-quart casserole in a preheated 350° oven for 45 minutes.

Makes 12 servings (4 cups)

	Calories	Carbo-hydrate (gm)	Protein (gm)	Total Fat (gm)	Saturated Fat (gm)	Choles-terol (mg)
Total	797.1	147.1	26.3	14.3	3.7	61.2
Per Serving	66.4	12.3	2.2	1.2	0.3	5.1

gm = grams; mg = milligrams. Nutritional figures are approximate. Figures are based on findings of U.S. Department of Agriculture.

Seafood Supreme

If you are now a seafood fan, this section is for you. If you are *not* . . . then this section is *especially* for you. It's quite possible that most overweights who claim to dislike fish have never really had it — good fish, that is.

If your seafood-sampling history is limited to frozen fish sticks, diner-fried fish fillets of indeterminate species, or the Friday fish special dished up in the company or school cafeteria, then you should count yourself among the vast number of Americans who have never had really good fish.

What is good fish? To begin with, it must be absolutely fresh. Fish that smells fishy isn't fresh —

because really fresh fish has no odor. The admonition that fish must be fresh doesn't mean you have to catch you own or barter with a charter boat operator down at the docks. And it doesn't mean that you must limit your marketing to fancy fish stores. Perfectly good fresh fish is available bargain-priced in your supermarket freezer case. Yes, frozen fish can be the freshest of all — if it has been properly handled. Frozen fish is frequently processed right on the commercial vessel on which it is caught. However, partial thawing or careless handling anywhere along the distribution route can result in subquality seafood when you thaw it out at home. If frozen seafood shows signs of mishandling when you thaw it out, simply wrap it in plastic and return it to the store for a refund.

Good seafood is also properly cooked. And here's where lots of perfectly fine fish winds up a culinary casualty. Unlike meat, fish doesn't need cooking to make it tender. The purpose of cooking fish is to develop its fine flavor. Overcooking — either too much or for too long — only results in toughness, dryness, and unpleasant flavor. Fish that has been overfloured and carelessly tossed into a skillet full of fat is not only fattening, it is unappetizing in taste, texture, and appearance. If that's the sort of seafood you've been exposed to, it is time to give fish a fighting chance.

Why the Emphasis on Fish for Slimming?

Anyone who has a nodding acquaintance with dieting knows that seafood turns up with sometimes monotonous frequency on most lose-weight plans. The reason is that seafood is the slimmest of all main course choices, the one that's highest in protein and lowest in fat.

All fish, even so-called fatty fish, is low calorie when compared with most meat. Flounder, a lean fish, is only 308 calories a pound compared with 1,818 calories for rib roast, with a comparable protein content. Mackerel, which is a fat fish, has only 866 calories a pound and *more* protein that rib roast.

Buying Fresh Fish

Here is the advice of the National Marine Fisheries Service* on selecting the freshest fish. Look for these qualities:

Flesh: Firm flesh, not separating from the bones, indicates fish are fresh and have been handled carefully.

Odor: Fresh and mild. A fish just taken from the water has practically no fishy odor. The fishy odor becomes more pronounced with passage of time, but it should not be disagreeably strong when the fish is bought.

Eyes: Bright, clear, and full. The eyes of fresh fish

---

*"Let's Cook Fish: A Complete Guide to Fish Cookery." *Fishery Market Development Series No. 8.* U.S. Department of Interior, Fish and Wildlife Service, Bureau of Commercial Fisheries, U.S. Govt. Printing Office, 60 cents.

are bright and transparent; as the fish becomes stale, the eyes become cloudy and often turn pink. When fish are fresh, the eyes often protrude, but with increasing staleness, the eyes tend to become sunken.

Gills: Red and free from slime. The color gradually fades with age to a light pink, then gray, and finally brownish or greenish.

Skin: Shiny, with color unfaded. When first taken from the water, most fish have an irridescent appearance. Each species has its characteristic markings and colors that fade and become less pronounced as the fish loses freshness.

Fresh fillets, steaks, and chunks have the following characteristics:

Flesh: Fresh-cut in appearance. It should be firm in texture without traces of browning or drying around the edges,

Odor: Fresh and mild.

Wrapping: If the fillets, steaks, or chunks are wrapped, the wrapping should be a moisture/vapor-proof material. There should be little or no airspace between the fish and the wrapping.

Buying Frozen Fish

High-quality frozen fish that are properly processed, packaged, and held at 0° or below will remain in good condition for relatively long periods of time. Frozen fish of good quality have the following characteristics:

Flesh: The flesh should be solidly frozen when bought. The flesh should have no discoloration or freezer burn. Virtually all deterioration in quality is prevented when fish are properly held in the frozen state. Frozen fish that have been thawed and then refrozen are poorer in quality.

Odor: Frozen fish should have little or no odor. A strong fish odor means poor quality.

Wrapping: Most frozen fillets, steaks, chunks, portions, and sticks are wrapped either individually or in packages of various weights. The wrapping should be of moisture/vapor-proof material. There should be little or no airspace between the fish and the wrapping.

How Much Fish Should You Buy?

Whole: This is fish as it comes from the water. Before cooking, the fish must be scaled and gutted. Usually the head, tail and fins are removed. The fish may then be cooked, filleted, or cut into steaks or chunks. Allow 2/3 to 3/4 pound per serving.

Dressed: This is fish with scales and entrails removed. Usually the head, tail, and fins are also removed. The fish may then be cooked whole, filleted, or cut into steaks or chunks. (The smaller size fish are called pan-dressed and are ready to cook as purchased). About 1/3 to 1/2 pound equals one serving.

Fillets: The flesh of the fish cut lengthwise away from the backbone. They are boneless, usually skinless and ready to cook as purchased. Allow 1/4 pound per serving.

Steaks: These are cross-section slices from large dressed fish cut 1/2 to 1 inch thick. A cross-section of the backbone is the only bone in a steak. They are ready to cook as purchased. Allow 1/4 to 1/3 pound per serving.

Chunks: These are cross-sections of large dressed fish. A cross-section of the backbone is the only bone in a chunk. They are ready to cook as purchased. Allow 1/3 to 1/4 pound per serving.

What Dieters Should Avoid

Although fish is the best calorie and nutrition bargain you can buy, there are some types of frozen fish that dieters should stay away from. Fish is often frozen already breaded as a "convenience" to busy homemakers. What you get when you pay for already-breaded fish is a lot of breading and not much fish. You also get a lot of extra calories.

Raw breaded fish portions: These are portions cut from frozen fish blocks, coated with a batter, breaded, packaged, and frozen. Raw breaded fish portions generally contain only 75 percent fish.

Fried fish sticks: These are cut from frozen fish blocks. They are coated with a batter, then fried in fat, and frozen. Fried fish sticks are only 60 percent fish.

Recipes

Smothered Fish Steaks

6 fish steaks (2 lb.)
8-oz. can sliced
    mushrooms,
    drained, reserving
    liquid
1-lb. can tomatoes,
    drained, reserving
    liquid
1/4 cup finely chopped
    onion

1 garlic clove,
    minced
1/4 cup water
2 tbsp. flour
3/4 tsp. salt
1/8 tsp. coarse freshly
    ground black
    pepper

Arrange the fish in a shallow baking dish. Spoon the mushrooms, tomatoes, chopped onion, and minced garlic over the fish. In a bowl, combine the reserved liquid from the mushrooms and tomatoes with 1/4 cup water. Mix in the flour, salt, and pepper. Pour this mixture over the fish. Cover and bake in a preheated 375° oven for 15 minutes. Then remove the cover and bake 15 to 20 minutes longer, until the fish flakes when tested with a fork.   *Makes 6 servings*

	Calories	Carbo-hydrate (gm)	Protein (gm)	Total Fat (gm)	Saturated Fat (gm)	Cholesterol (mg)
Total	1750.3	39.9	235.0	66.1	21.3	543.7
Per Serving	291.7	6.7	39.2	11.0	3.6	90.6

Turkish Baked Sea Steaks

4 cod or other fish
    steaks (1 1/2 lb.)
Mixed pickling spices,
    or broken bay
    leaves
4 tbsp. lemon juice or
    white wine

1/4 tsp. salt
Dash freshly
    ground pepper
Dash paprika
4 parsley sprigs
4 lemon wedges

Spread the steaks in a single layer in a small, shallow baking pan just large enough to hold them. Tuck the pickling spices or bay leaves under each steak. Sprinkle with lemon or wine; season with salt, pepper and paprika. Bake uncovered in a preheated 350° oven 15 to 25 minutes, depending on thickness, until the steaks flake easily. Baste occasionally with the juices in the pan. Spoon the juices over the steaks and garnish with parsley and lemon wedges.

Makes 4 servings

	Calories	Carbo-hydrate (gm)	Protein (gm)	Total Fat (gm)	Saturated Fat (gm)	Choles-terol (mg)
Total	1175.0	5.0	192.3	40.0	8.0	552.0
Per Serving	293.8	1.3	48.1	10.0	2.0	138.0

Sea Steak Teriyaki

6 swordfish or other fish steaks (1½ lb.)
2 tbsp. fresh lemon juice
2 tbsp. soy sauce
½ tsp. dry mustard
½ tsp. ground ginger
⅛ tsp. garlic powder

Place the fish in a shallow pan. Combine the remaining ingredients. Pour them over the fish and let it stand at room temperature for 1 hour, turning it once. Remove the fish steaks from the marinade and place them on a broiler pan. Broil 3 inches from the heat source for 5 minutes. Then turn them over, brush them with the marinade, and broil them for another 5 to 10 minutes, until the fish flakes easily when tested with a fork.

Makes 6 servings

	Calories	Carbo-hydrate (gm)	Protein (gm)	Total Fat (gm)	Saturated Fat (gm)	Choles-terol (mg)
Total	1227.2	4.4	194.1	40.0	0.0	544.0
Per Serving	204.5	0.7	32.4	6.7	0.0	90.7

---

gm = grams; mg = milligrams. Nutritional figures are approximate. Figures are based on findings of U.S. Department of Agriculture.

Oven-Fried Fish Fillets I

1 egg
2 tbsp. corn or safflower
oil

½ cup seasoned
bread crumbs
4 fish fillets (1 lb.)

Whip the egg and oil together with a fork. Pour this mixture onto a plate. Place the bread crumbs on another plate. Dip the fillets first into the egg mixture and then into the bread crumbs so they are lightly coated. Place the breaded fillets on a nonstick cookie sheet or other shallow pan with nonstick coating and bake them in a preheated 450° oven for 10 to 12 minutes, until they are golden and cooked through.

Makes 4 servings

	Calories	Carbohydrate (gm)	Protein (gm)	Total Fat (gm)	Saturated Fat (gm)	Cholesterol (mg)
Total	1441.8	36.5	151.1	73.8	15.2	664.9
Per Serving	360.5	9.1	37.7	18.5	3.8	166.2

Oven-Fried Fish Fillets II

4 fish fillets (1 lb.)
½ cup French or Italian
salad dressing
(regular, not diet)

½ cup unseasoned
bread crumbs

Marinate the fish fillets in the dressing for 15 minutes, turning frequently. Spray a nonstick cookie sheet or shallow baking pan with vegetable coating for no-fat frying. Sprinkle the crumbs on a shallow plate. Press each well-moistened fillet in the crumbs, coating both sides lightly. Then arrange in a single layer on the cookie sheet. Bake in a preheated 450° oven for 5 to 6 minutes. Carefully turn fillets with a spatula and continue baking another 5 to 6 minutes. *Makes 4 servings*

	Calories	Carbohydrate (gm)	Protein (gm)	Total Fat (gm)	Saturated Fat (gm)	Cholesterol (mg)
Total	1227.9	48.5	134.4	53.2	9.8	370.3
Per Serving	307.00	12.1	33.6	13.3	2.5	92.6

Shrimp Bisque

¼ cup finely chopped
onion
¼ cup finely chopped
celery
¼ cup water
2 tbsp. flour

1 tsp. butter-flavored
salt
¼ tsp. paprika
Dash white pepper
4 cups skim milk
14 oz. cooked shrimp,
coarsely
chopped

Place the onion, celery, and water in a nonstick skillet.
Cook until the vegetables are tender. Stir in the flour
and seasonings. Add the milk to the skillet and cook
the entire mixture over low heat, stirring constantly,
until it is thick. Fold in the shrimp. Continue cooking
just until the shrimp is heated through; serve it at once.

Makes 6 servings

	Calories	Carbo-hydrate (gm)	Protein (gm)	Total Fat (gm)	Saturated Fat (gm)	Choles-terol (mg)
Total	787.2	63.4	108.0	4.8	0.0	616.5
Per Serving	131.2	10.6	18.0	0.8	0.0	102.7

Tuna with Grapes

⅔ cup water
½ cup instant rice
1 vegetable bouillon
cube
¼ cup finely chopped
celery
2 tbsp. snipped parsley
2 tbsp. all-purpose flour
½ tsp. salt
1 cup evaporated
skim milk

7-oz. can water-
packed tuna,
drained and
broken into
chunks
½ cup seedless
green grapes,
halved
2 tbsp. dry white
wine
1 tbsp. lemon juice

Bring the ⅔ cup water to a boil in a saucepan. Add the
rice, bouillon, celery, and parsley, and cook for 2

minutes. Spray 4 individual casseroles with vegetable coating and spoon the rice mixture into them. Then, combine the flour, salt, and evaporated milk in a saucepan. Cook over low heat, stirring constantly, until the mixture is thick and bubbly. Remove the pot from the heat and stir in the remaining ingredients. Spoon this mixture into the casseroles over the rice. Bake in a preheated 350° oven for 20 minutes.

Makes 4 servings

	Calories	Carbo-hydrate (gm)	Protein (gm)	Total Fat (gm)	Saturated Fat (gm)	Choles-terol (mg)
Total	1076.3	134.2	94.9	30.3	13.2	204.0
Per Serving	269.1	33.6	23.7	7.6	3.3	51.0

Hot Tuna Sandwiches

1 tbsp. diet margarine
1½ tsp. minced green pepper
1 tsp. minced onion
4 eggs, slightly beaten
¼ cup skim milk
½ tsp. salt

7-oz. can water-packed tuna (lobster or crabmeat may be used)
4 slices toasted high-fiber or protein bread

Preheat a nonstick saucepan over low heat for 2 minutes. Melt the margarine. Add the green pepper and onion and sauté about 5 minutes. Remove the pan from the heat and add the eggs, milk, salt, and tuna. Cook the mixture over low heat for about 10 minutes, stirring constantly, until it is thick and creamy. Serve over the toast.

Makes 4 servings

	Calories	Carbo-hydrate (gm)	Protein (gm)	Total Fat (gm)	Saturated Fat (gm)	Choles-terol (mg)
Total	868.7	46.8	92.0	34.8	9.6	1138.9
Per Serving	217.2	11.7	23.0	8.7	2.4	284.7

---

gm = grams; mg = milligrams. Nutritional figures are approximate. Figures are based on findings of U.S. Department of Agriculture.

Unforbidden Sweets

Yes, sugar is an artificial sweetener, too. It's pure, refined, processed calories with no redeeming nutritional value, perhaps the most abused and overused additive there is. Of all the things we eat that cost us calories, nothing offers less sustained appetite satisfaction or is burned up or turned to fat by the body as quickly as sugar. Mother Nature never created foods as sweet as many of the sweets we eat. There probably is no need for processed sugar in human nutrition. In fact, throughout most of human history, sugar simply did not exist.

Recipes

Apples au Vin Rouge

4 baking apples
½ cup bottled
    unsweetened red or
    purple grape juice

¼ cup red wine
½ tsp. pumpkin pie
    spice

Core apples and remove about one inch of peel from the top. Arrange them in a baking dish just large enough to hold them. Pour on the grape juice and wine. Sprinkle the apples with spice. Bake the apples in a preheated 350° oven about 30 to 45 minutes, basting frequently with the sauce. *Makes 4 servings*

	Calories	Carbohydrate (gm)	Protein (gm)	Total Fat (gm)	Saturated Fat (gm)	Cholesterol (mg)
Total	383.8	94.0	0.5	0.0	0.0	0.0
Per Serving	96.0	23.5	0.1	0.0	0.0	0.0

Raisin-Stuffed Baked Apples

4 cooking apples
4 tbsp. raisins
½ tsp. cinnamon

¾ cup water
1 tsp. lemon juice

Core the apples then peel them only ¼ of the way down from the stem. Set the apples in a nonstick baking pan. Add 1 tablespoon of the raisins to the cavity of each apple. Sprinkle with cinnamon. Combine the water with the lemon juice and pour it over the apples. Bake the apples in a preheated 375° oven, basting occasionally with the liquid from the pan until they are tender and easily pierced with a fork, about 1 hour.

Makes 4 servings

	Calories	Carbohydrate (gm)	Protein (gm)	Total Fat (gm)	Saturated Fat (gm)	Cholesterol (mg)
Total	272.1	103.2	1.3	0.0	0.0	0.0
Per Serving	68.0	25.8	0.3	0.0	0.0	0.0

gm = grams; mg = milligrams. Nutritional figures are approximate. Figures are based on findings of U.S. Department of Agriculture.

Frosty Fruit Whip

⅔ cup evaporated skim milk

8-oz. pkg. low-calorie cream cheese, softened

16-oz. can unsweetened fruit cocktail, drained

1 banana, sliced

2 tbsp. fresh lemon juice

Pour the evaporated skim milk into a mixing bowl and chill in the freezer until ice forms at the edges. In the meantime, beat the cream cheese until it is smooth and creamy. Stir in the fruit cocktail and banana. Using chilled beaters, whip the frosted milk in the chilled bowl with the high speed of your mixer until fluffy. Add the lemon juice and continue whipping until the milk is stiff. Fold the whipped milk into the fruit. Spoon the mixture into a 9-inch square pan and freeze for about 3 hours until it is firm. Cut it into 9 squares for serving.

Makes 9 servings

	Calories	Carbo-hydrate (gm)	Protein (gm)	Total Fat (gm)	Saturated Fat (gm)	Choles-terol (mg)
Total	1210.5	107.4	31.5	61.2	39.3	219.5
Per Serving	134.5	11.9	3.5	6.8	4.4	24.4

Spiced Fruit Compote

16-oz. can juice-packed unsweetened fruit cocktail

2 tbsp. raisins

½-in. stick cinnamon

4 to 6 whole cloves

Combine all of the ingredients and heat to boiling. Remove cinnamon and cloves and chill before serving.

Makes 4 servings

	Calories	Carbo-hydrate (gm)	Protein (gm)	Total Fat (gm)	Saturated Fat (gm)	Choles-terol (mg)
Total	218.4	54.2	2.2	0.4	0.0	0.0
Per Serving	54.6	13.6	0.6	0.1	0.0	0.0

Fresh Applesauce

4 or 5 McIntosh apples
(about 1 lb.), peeled,
cored, and chunked
3 or 4 tbsp. lemon juice
(or ¼ of a 100-mg.
ascorbic acid
tablet, crushed)

Pinch salt
Few drops vanilla
¼ tsp. cinnamon
(optional)

Process the apple chunks in covered blender with lemon juice or crushed ascorbic acid tablet (these will keep applesauce from turning brown). Blend in the salt, vanilla and cinnamon. Pour into a serving bowl and chill. *Makes 4 servings*

	Calories	Carbo-hydrate (gm)	Protein (gm)	Total Fat (gm)	Saturated Fat (gm)	Choles-terol (mg)
Total	331.0	84.6	0.4	0.0	0.0	0.0
Per Serving	82.8	21.2	0.1	0.0	0.0	0.0

Pineapplesauce

4 or 5 cooking apples
(about 1 lb.), cored,
peeled, sliced
16-oz. can unsweetened,
juice-packed
crushed pineapple

Vanilla, salt or
cinnamon to
taste

Combine all of the ingredients in a covered saucepan and simmer until apples are tender, about 20 minutes. Stir sauce until smooth and chill before serving.
Makes 8 servings

	Calories	Carbo-hydrate (gm)	Protein (gm)	Total Fat (gm)	Saturated Fat (gm)	Choles-terol (mg)
Total	547.0	141.4	1.2	0.4	0.0	0.0
Per Serving	68.4	17.7	0.2	0.1	0.0	0.0

gm = grams; mg = milligrams. Nutritional figures are approximate. Figures are based on findings of U.S. Department of Agriculture.

Easy No-Fat Crepe Making

A special crepe pan is nice to have around but not really necessary for making crepes at home. Excellent crepes can be made easily in an ordinary skillet or omelet pan — with no added fat. Choose a small 6- or 7-inch pan with a nonstick surface. Apply cooking spray to the pan until the surface is slick and wet. Preheat the pan over a moderate flame until a slight vapor rises from the surface. When the surface is hot enough, a drop of water will bounce on it. Make 1 crepe at a time. Pour about 2 tablespoons of batter into the pan. Rotate the pan quickly to spread the batter as thinly as possible. Cook about 30 to 40 seconds, until the surface of the crepe is dry. Flip the pan over onto a clean towel and let the crepe drop out. Continue making crepes, one at a time, until all the batter is used. Apply cooking spray to the skillet before pouring the batter for each new crepe.

High-Protein Egg Crepes

3 eggs
6 tbsp. all-purpose flour
½ cup skim milk

2 tbsp. diet margarine, at room temperature
Few drops vanilla (optional)

Combine all of the ingredients in a blender or mixing bowl and beat smooth. Let the batter rest 20 minutes. Follow crepe making directions on this page. Fill with fruit, and top with one of the sauces in this book. Or use as a base for any crepe recipe.

Makes 12 crepes (1 per serving)

	Calories	Carbo-hydrate (gm)	Protein (gm)	Total Fat (gm)	Saturated Fat (gm)	Choles-terol (mg)
Total	438.0	39.3	25.8	18.3	6.0	758.5
Per Serving	36.5	3.3	2.2	1.5	0.5	63.2

Eggless High-Protein Crepes

½ cup frozen (defrosted)
or liquid no-
cholesterol egg
substitute

4 tbsp. all-purpose
flour

6 tbsp. skim milk

Combine all of the ingredients and beat smooth. Let
the batter rest 20 minutes. Follow the crepe making directions in this section. Use as a base for any crepe
recipe.   *Makes 8 crepes (1 per serving)*

	Calories	Carbo-hydrate (gm)	Protein (gm)	Total Fat (gm)	Saturated Fat (gm)	Choles-terol (mg)
Total	332.0	26.2	18.4	15.2	0.0	2.2
Per Serving	41.5	3.3	2.3	1.9	0.0	0.3

Dessert Blintzes

2 cups 99% fat-free pot-
style cottage
cheese

2 tsp. vanilla

¼ tsp. butter-flavored
salt

2 eggs

12 High-Protein Egg
Crepes (recipe in
this section)

16-oz. can crushed
unsweetened
juice-packed
pineapple,
undrained

1 tsp. arrowroot

Combine cottage cheese, vanilla, salt and eggs. Beat
until smooth. Spoon the cheese filling into the crepes
and roll up. Arrange the rolled crepes in a nonstick
pan that has been sprayed with a vegetable coating.
Cover lightly with foil. Bake in a preheated 300° oven
20 minutes. Meanwhile, combine undrained pineapple
and arrowroot in a saucepan. Cook and stir until the
sauce is thick and bubbling. To serve, spoon the pineapple sauce over the hot blintzes. *Makes 12 servings*

	Calories	Carbo-hydrate (gm)	Protein (gm)	Total Fat (gm)	Saturated Fat (gm)	Choles-terol (mg)
Total	1190.0	111.7	99.0	34.7	12.4	1301.3
Per Serving	99.2	9.3	8.3	2.9	1.0	108.4

Real Orange Gelatin

1 tbsp. unflavored
    gelatin
1/4 cup cold water
1 cup boiling water

6-oz. can
    unsweetened
    frozen orange
    juice
    concentrate,
    partly defrosted
    but undiluted

Combine the gelatin and cold water in a blender. Wait 1 minute, until gelatin is soft, then add the boiling water, cover and blend on high speed until all granules are dissolved. Scrape down sides frequently. Add the orange juice, cover and blend until smooth. Pour into dessert cups and chill until set. *Makes 4 servings*

Hint: For a delightful variation on this recipe, fold some thin sliced banana into each cup when the gelatin has chilled enough to become syrupy. Then chill until set.

	Calories	Carbo-hydrate (gm)	Protein (gm)	Total Fat (gm)	Saturated Fat (gm)	Choles-terol (mg)
Total	385.0	87.0	11.0	0.0	0.0	0.0
Per Serving	96.2	21.8	2.8	0.0	0.0	0.0

Brandied Peach Sherbet

3 tbsp. peach brandy
1 envelope unflavored
    gelatin

16-oz. can
    unsweetened
    juice-packed
    peaches,
    drained
    reserving juice
Pinch salt (or
    butter-flavored
    salt)

Put the brandy in a blender container. Sprinkle on the gelatin and wait 1 minute until the granules soften. Measure the peach juice and add cold water if necessary to equal 1 1/2 cups. Heat the juice and water to boiling. Pour into the blender, cover, and blend until all the gelatin granules are dissolved. Add the peaches and salt; cover and blend smooth. Pour the mixture into a shallow metal dish and freeze only until slushy. Break up into a mixing bowl and beat until fluffy. Freeze firm. Soften briefly before serving. *Makes 8 servings*

	Calories	Carbo-hydrate (gm)	Protein (gm)	Total Fat (gm)	Saturated Fat (gm)	Choles-terol (mg)
Total	255.0	42.4	2.2	0.4	0.0	0.0
Per Serving	32.0	5.3	0.3	0.1	0.0	0.0

Easy Blender Frozen Yogurt

1/2 envelope unflavored gelatin
1/4 cup cold water
1 cup boiling water
8 oz. low-fat vanilla yogurt

2/3 cup instant nonfat dry milk powder (or 1/2 cup non-instant dry milk)
1/4 tsp. salt
6-oz. can unsweetened frozen orange juice concentrate, partially thawed

In a blender container, combine the gelatin and cold water. Wait 1 minute for the gelatin to soften, then add the boiling water. Cover and blend on high speed until all the gelatin granules are dissolved. Add the yogurt, milk powder, salt and orange juice and blend smooth. Pour the mixture into a shallow metal dish and freeze until slushy. Remove from the freezer and quickly beat smooth. Return to the freezer and freeze firm. Allow the frozen yogurt to soften briefly at room temperature before serving. *Makes 12 servings*

	Calories	Carbo-hydrate (gm)	Protein (gm)	Total Fat (gm)	Saturated Fat (gm)	Choles-terol (mg)
Total	660.9	123.4	32.0	4.0	2.0	30.0
Per Serving	55.1	10.3	2.7	0.3	0.2	2.5

gm = grams; mg = milligrams. Nutritional figures are approximate. Figures are based on findings of U.S. Department of Agriculture.

Fluffy Grape Dessert

1 envelope unflavored gelatin	1¼ cups bottled unsweetened grape juice
½ cup cold water	⅛ tsp. salt

Sprinkle the gelatin over the water in a saucepan and let it stand until the gelatin softens. Place the pan over low heat for about 3 minutes, stirring constantly until the gelatin dissolves. Remove the pan from the heat and stir in the grape juice and salt. Chill the mixture, stirring occasionally, until it has thickened slightly. Pour it into a chilled bowl and beat it with your electric mixer or rotary beater until it is light and fluffy and doubled in volume. Spoon the whipped mixture into dessert dishes and chill until firm. *Makes 4 servings*

	Calories	Carbo-hydrate (gm)	Protein (gm)	Total Fat (gm)	Saturated Fat (gm)	Choles-terol (mg)
Total	231.3	52.5	7.3	0.0	0.0	0.0
Per Serving	57.8	13.1	1.8	0.0	0.0	0.0

Icebox Fruit 'n' Rice Pudding

½ cup instant rice
2 cups unsweetened canned pineapple juice (not fresh or frozen)
¼ tsp. salt or butter-flavored salt
1 envelope unflavored gelatin
4 tbsp. cold water
8-oz. can unsweetened fruit cocktail, undrained

1 eating orange, peeled, seeded, and cut in chunks
1 red apple, cored and diced (unpeeled)
1 ripe pear, cored and diced (unpeeled)
1 small ripe banana, peeled and sliced
3 tsp. Curacao or any orange liqueur (optional)

Heat the rice, pineapple juice, and salt to boiling in a saucepan. Remove from heat, cover and set aside 15 to 20 minutes until the rice is soft. Meanwhile, sprinkle the gelatin over the cold water and set aside to soften. When the rice and gelatin are both soft, stir the gelatin mixture into the rice. Heat gently until the gelatin granules are thoroughly dissolved. Remove from heat and stir in the remaining ingredients. Spoon into a loaf pan and chill several hours until set. *Makes 8 servings*

	Calories	Carbo-hydrate (gm)	Protein (gm)	Total Fat (gm)	Saturated Fat (gm)	Choles-terol (mg)
Total	854.0	186.4	13.8	1.2	0.0	0.0
Per Serving	106.8	23.3	1.7	0.2	0.0	0.0

Jam from Frozen Berries

2½ cups frozen unsweetened berries (strawberries, blueberries, raspberries), defrosted

¼ cup unsweetened frozen grape juice concentrate, defrosted but undiluted

1 envelope unflavored gelatin

1½ tsp. cornstarch

Combine all of the ingredients in a saucepan. Wait 1 minute for the gelatin granules to soften, then cook and stir until the mixture thickens. Cool, then pour into airtight containers and chill until set. Store in the refrigerator. *Makes 2 cups (32 servings)*

	Calories	Carbo-hydrate (gm)	Protein (gm)	Total Fat (gm)	Saturated Fat (gm)	Choles-terol (mg)
Total	267.1	58.9	8.9	2.5	0.0	0.0
Per Serving	8.3	1.8	0.3	0.1	0.0	0.0

gm = grams; mg = milligrams. Nutritional figures are approximate. Figures are based on findings of U.S. Department of Agriculture.

Peach Sugarless Jelly

3 cups canned
  unsweetened peach
  nectar (available in
  health food stores)

1 tbsp. cornstarch
1 envelope
  unflavored
  gelatin

Combine the nectar and cornstarch in a saucepan.
Sprinkle the gelatin on the nectar mixture. Stir until the
gelatin and cornstarch are dissolved. Wait 1 minute,
then heat to boiling, stirring frequently. Boil 1 minute.
Cool, then pour into airtight containers and refrigerate.

Makes 3 cups (48 servings)

	Calories	Carbo-hydrate (gm)	Protein (gm)	Total Fat (gm)	Saturated Fat (gm)	Choles-terol (mg)
Total	385.0	93.0	7.5	0.0	0.0	0.0
Per Serving	8.0	1.9	0.2	0.0	0.0	0.0

Jiffy Marmalade

1 envelope unflavored
  gelatin
1/4 cup cold water
1 cup boiling water

6-oz. can frozen
  unsweetened
  orange juice
  concentrate,
  partly defrosted
  but not diluted
1 orange, peeled,
  seeded and
  diced
1/4 of the orange peel

Sprinkle the gelatin on the cold water in a blender container. Wait 1 minute, then add the boiling water. Cover
and blend on high speed until the gelatin is dissolved,
scraping sides of container. Add the orange concentrate and blend smooth. Add the orange chunks and
orange peel; blend until coarsely chopped. Cool, then
pour into an airtight container and refrigerate.

Makes about 1 1/2 cups (24 servings)

	Calories	Carbo-hydrate (gm)	Protein (gm)	Total Fat (gm)	Saturated Fat (gm)	Choles-terol (mg)
Total	400.0	103.0	12.0	0.0	0.0	0.0
Per Serving	16.7	4.3	0.5	0.0	0.0	0.0

Basic Piecrust

½ cup all-purpose flour   2 tbsp. salad oil
Pinch salt   1 tbsp. ice water

Stir all of the ingredients together in a bowl with a fork.
Then knead the mixture lightly until the pastry forms a
ball. Flatten out the dough; wrap it in waxed paper and
chill thoroughly. Roll the dough out on a lightly floured
board. This will line an 8-inch pie plate. For a two-crust
pie, double the recipe.   *Makes 8 servings*

	Calories	Carbo-hydrate (gm)	Protein (gm)	Total Fat (gm)	Saturated Fat (gm)	Choles-terol (mg)
Total	477.5	47.5	6.5	28.5	2.0	0.0
Per Serving	59.7	5.9	0.8	3.6	0.3	0.0

Buttery Pastry Shell

1 cup flour   2 tbsp. diet
1½ tsp. butter-flavored   margarine
    salt   2 tbsp. butter

Sift the flour and butter-flavored salt into a bowl. Cut in
the margarine and butter. Knead the mixture just long
enough for the dough to form a ball. Roll the dough out
thinly on a well-floured board. This makes enough for
an 8-inch double-crust pie.   *Makes 8 servings*

	Calories	Carbo-hydrate (gm)	Protein (gm)	Total Fat (gm)	Saturated Fat (gm)	Choles-terol (mg)
Total	757.5	95.3	13.3	36.0	14.8	70.8
Per Serving	94.7	11.9	1.7	4.5	1.9	8.9

*gm = grams; mg = milligrams. Nutritional figures are approximate.
Figures are based on findings of U.S. Department of Agriculture.*

Graham Cracker Crust

²/₃ cup graham cracker   2 tbsp. diet
     crumbs   margarine

Lightly combine the graham cracker crumbs and diet margarine. Press them firmly into the bottom of an 8- or 9-inch nonstick pie pan. This crust is quite tender. For a sturdier crust, quick-bake it in a preheated 425° oven for 6 to 8 minutes. Watch the crust — it burns easily. Cool before filling.   *Makes 8 servings*

	Calories	Carbo-hydrate (gm)	Protein (gm)	Total Fat (gm)	Saturated Fat (gm)	Choles-terol (mg)
Total	390.4	55.4	5.3	19.9	2.0	0.0
Per Serving	48.8	6.9	0.7	2.5	0.3	0.0

Pink Strawberry No-Bake Cream Cheese Pie

Graham Cracker
     Crust (recipe on this
     page)
2 tsp. vanilla
1 tbsp. lemon juice
1 cup unsweetened
     bottled red grape
     juice, undiluted
1 envelope unflavored
     gelatin

8-oz. pkg. low-
     calorie cream
     cheese or
     Neufchatel
     cheese
¼ tsp. salt or butter-
     flavored salt
¼ tsp. grated lemon
     peel
1 cup ice cubes
     Jellied Berry
     Topping (recipe
     in this section)

Prepare Graham Cracker Crust. Combine the vanilla, lemon juice and 1 tablespoon of the grape juice in a blender. Sprinkle on the gelatin and wait 1 minute. Meanwhile, heat the remaining grape juice to boiling. Pour it into the blender. Cover and blend on high speed until the gelatin is dissolved (scrape sides of container frequently.) Add the cream cheese, salt and lemon peel. Cover and blend smooth. Add the ice cubes, a few at a time, and continue to blend until the ice is thoroughly dissolved. Spoon the filling into the crust and chill. (Mixture will be thick and partly set already.) Prepare the topping. When the filling is thoroughly set, arrange the topping on it. Chill again until topping is set. *Makes 8 servings*

	Calories	Carbohydrate (gm)	Protein (gm)	Total Fat (gm)	Saturated Fat (gm)	Cholesterol (mg)
Total	1335.8	151.1	33.3	68.9	34.0	168.0
Per Serving	167.0	18.9	4.2	8.6	4.3	21.0

Jellied Berry Topping

¾ cup ice-cold bottled unsweetened red grape juice (purple or white grape juice may be substituted)

1½ tsp. (½ envelope) unflavored gelatin
1 cup sliced strawberries (or other fresh fruit such as peaches, blueberries, or raspberries)

Put 2 tablespoons of the grape juice in a small saucepan and sprinkle with the gelatin. Wait 1 minute, until the gelatin is soft, then heat gently until the gelatin melts. Remove from heat and stir in the remaining cold fruit juice. Refrigerate until syrupy. Arrange the berries on top of chilled filling (filling must be set), then spoon the gelatin mixture to cover the fruit with a jellied glaze. Chill until set.

Makes about 1½ cups (8 servings)

	Calories	Carbohydrate (gm)	Protein (gm)	Total Fat (gm)	Saturated Fat (gm)	Cholesterol (mg)
Total	191.4	44.5	4.9	1.0	0.0	0.0
Per Serving	23.9	5.6	0.6	0.1	0.0	0.0

gm = grams; mg = milligrams. Nutritional figures are approximate. Figures are based on findings of U.S. Department of Agriculture.

Orange Cheese Pie

Graham Cracker
Crust (recipe in this
section)
2 egg whites
Pinch salt
8-oz. pkg. diet cream
cheese or
Neufchatel cheese
2 whole eggs

6-oz. can
unsweetened
frozen orange
juice
concentrate,
defrosted but not
diluted
1 tbsp. arrowroot
1 tsp. vanilla
1/2 tsp. pumpkin pie
spice

Prepare Graham Cracker Crust. In a mixing bowl, beat the egg whites and salt until stiff peaks form. Combine the remaining ingredients in a blender. Cover and blend smooth. Gently but thoroughly fold the blender mixture into egg whites. Spoon into the crust. Bake in a preheated 300° oven until the filling is set. Cool at room temperature, then chill.   *Makes 8 servings*

	Calories	Carbo-hydrate (gm)	Protein (gm)	Total Fat (gm)	Saturated Fat (gm)	Choles-terol (mg)
Total	1500.4	150.4	46.3	79.9	38.0	672.0
Per Serving	187.6	18.8	5.8	10.0	4.8	84.0

South Seas Pineapple Pie

Basic Piecrust (recipe
in this section)
1 eating orange,
peeled, seeded and
diced
20-oz. can unsweetened
juice-packed
crushed pineapple,
undrained

2 tbsp. granulated
tapioca
4 tbsp. golden
raisins
2 tbsp. grated
orange peel
(optional)
Pinch salt

Line an 8-inch pie plate with Basic Piecrust. Combine

all of the filling ingredients thoroughly and spoon into the crust. Trim a sheet of aluminum foil to fit over the filling, so the crust will brown but the filling won't dry out. Bake in a preheated 425° oven for 30 to 45 minutes, until the crust is brown. Serve warm or chilled.

Makes 8 servings

	Calories	Carbo-hydrate (gm)	Protein (gm)	Total Fat (gm)	Saturated Fat (gm)	Choles-terol (mg)
Total	1047.3	187.5	10.3	28.9	2.0	0.0
Per Serving	130.9	23.4	1.3	3.6	0.3	0.0

Spiked Apricot Cheese Pie

1 tbsp. diet margarine
½ cup graham cracker crumbs
1 lb. 99% fat-free pot-style cottage cheese
⅓ cup peach or apricot liqueur
3 eggs
Pinch salt
½ cup golden raisins
½ cup dried apricot halves, finely chopped
Cinnamon

Spread the margarine over the bottom of a nonstick 8-inch pie pan. Sprinkle on the graham cracker crumbs and press firmly into the bottom. In a blender container, combine the cheese, liqueur, eggs and salt. Cover and blend smooth, scraping down sides well. Pour half of the mixture into the pie pan. Sprinkle the raisins and apricots evenly over the filling. Pour on remaining filling, covering all the fruit. Sprinkle with cinnamon. Bake in a preheated 325° oven about 45 to 55 minutes until the filling is set. Cool before serving.

Makes 10 servings

	Calories	Carbo-hydrate (gm)	Protein (gm)	Total Fat (gm)	Saturated Fat (gm)	Choles-terol (mg)
Total	1301.4	138.8	84.4	31.0	9.4	794.8
Per Serving	130.1	13.9	8.4	3.1	1.0	79.5

gm = grams; mg = milligrams. Nutritional figures are approximate. Figures are based on findings of U.S. Department of Agriculture.

Spiced Harvest Pie

Basic Piecrust (recipe
in this section)
20-oz. can unsweetened
pie-sliced apples
(not apple pie
filling), undrained
1/2 cup raisins
4 soft prunes, chopped
1 eating orange, peeled
and chopped

1 tbsp. minced
orange peel
1/4 cup orange liqueur
3 tbsp. arrowroot
1 tsp. mixed
pumpkin pie
spice, or: 1/2 tsp.
cinnamon, 1/4
tsp. nutmeg, 1/8
tsp. ground
cloves and 1/8
tsp. ginger
1/8 tsp. salt

Line an 8-inch pie plate with Basic Piecrust. Combine
the filling ingredients and mix well. Spoon the filling
into the crust. Invert another piepan over the filling to
protect it from burning. Bake in a preheated 425° oven
for 30 to 40 minutes.   *Makes 8 servings*

	Calories	Carbo-hydrate (gm)	Protein (gm)	Total Fat (gm)	Saturated Fat (gm)	Choles-terol (mg)
Total	1151.1	185.1	11.9	29.0	2.0	0.0
Per Serving	143.9	23.1	1.5	3.6	0.3	0.0

Apple-Raisin Pie

Buttery Pastry Shell
(the recipe is in this
section)
1 cup golden raisins
1 tbsp. cornstarch
1 tsp. ground
cinnamon

1/2 tsp. ground
nutmeg
1/4 tsp. butter-flavored
salt
5 cups cooking apples,
pared, cored, and
sliced

Roll out half the pastry and place it in an 8-inch pie
plate. In a bowl combine the raisins, cornstarch, cinnamon, nutmeg, butter-flavored salt, and apple slices.
Spoon this mixture into the pastry-lined pie plate. Roll

out the remaining pastry and place it on top for the top crust. Press the edges of the top and bottom crust together and flute them. Cut vents in the top crust to allow steam to escape. Bake the pie for 40 minutes in a preheated 425° oven until golden brown.

Makes 8 servings

	Calories	Carbo-hydrate (gm)	Protein (gm)	Total Fat (gm)	Saturated Fat (gm)	Choles-terol (mg)
Total	1621.8	321.7	16.9	360.3	14.8	70.8
Per Serving	202.7	40.2	2.1	45.0	1.9	8.9

Spicy Spiked Apple Pie

Basic Piecrust (recipe in this section)
20-oz. can unsweetened pie-sliced apples (not pie filling), undrained
½ cup raisins

1 sweet eating orange, seeded, peeled and diced
1 tsp. vanilla
2 tbsp. brandy (optional)
2 tbsp. arrowroot
Pinch salt
1½ tsp. pumpkin pie spice

Line an 8-inch pie plate with Basic Piecrust. Combine all of the filling ingredients thoroughly and spoon into the crust. Trim a sheet of aluminum foil to cover only the filling, so the crust will brown but the filling will not dry out. Bake in a preheated 425° oven for 30 to 40 minutes. Serve warm or chilled.

Makes 8 servings

	Calories	Carbo-hydrate (gm)	Protein (gm)	Total Fat (gm)	Saturated Fat (gm)	Choles-terol (mg)
Total	1026.1	155.1	10.9	29.0	2.0	0.0
Per Serving	128.3	19.4	1.4	3.6	0.3	0.0

gm = grams; mg = milligrams. Nutritional figures are approximate. Figures are based on findings of U.S. Department of Agriculture.

Slim-Down Shortcake

Sugar-Free
Strawberries for
Shortcake
3 cups sifted all-
purpose flour

3 tsp. baking powder
1 tsp. salt
½ cup diet margarine
1¼ cups skim milk

Prepare Sugar-Free Strawberries for Shortcake. Sift
the flour, baking powder and salt together into a bowl.
Cut in the margarine until the mixture resembles cornmeal. Add the milk and stir quickly with a fork until the
dry ingredients are moistened. Divide the dough in half
and press each half into an 8-inch nonstick layer cake
pan that has been sprayed with vegetable coating.
Bake the dough in a preheated 350° oven for about 15
minutes until it is golden brown. Remove the cakes
from the pans and spoon half the sliced berries over 1
layer. Place the second layer of cake over the berries
and then spoon the remaining berries on top.

Makes 8 servings

	Calories	Carbo-hydrate (gm)	Protein (gm)	Total Fat (gm)	Saturated Fat (gm)	Choles-terol (mg)
Total	1940.2	296.9	64.1	70.7	0.0	0.0
Per Serving	242.5	37.1	8.0	8.8	0.0	0.0

Sugar-Free Strawberries for Shortcake

1 qt. fresh strawberries,
hulled and sliced

1 cup unsweetened
bottled red
grape juice

Combine the 2 ingredients and chill until serving time.
Spoon the strawberries over Slim-Down Shortcake.

Makes 8 servings

	Calories	Carbo-hydrate (gm)	Protein (gm)	Total Fat (gm)	Saturated Fat (gm)	Choles-terol (mg)
Total	383.2	93.5	5.0	4.0	0.0	0.0
Per Serving	47.9	11.7	0.6	0.5	0.0	0.0

*gm = grams; mg = milligrams. Nutritional figures are approximate.
Figures are based on findings of U.S. Department of Agriculture.*

Orange Pumpkin Pie

Basic Piecrust (the
recipe is in this
section)
1 cup canned pumpkin
(not sweetened pie
filling)

2 eggs
¾ cup skim milk
6-oz. can frozen
orange juice
concentrate,
defrosted and
undiluted
½ tbsp. cornstarch
¼ tsp. salt
2 tsp. pumpkin pie
spice

Line an 8-inch pie plate with Basic Piecrust. Combine
the rest of the ingredients in a bowl and beat them
thoroughly. Pour the mixture into the prepared pastry
shell. Bake the pie for 1 hour in a preheated 350° oven.

Makes 8 servings

	Calories	Carbo-hydrate (gm)	Protein (gm)	Total Fat (gm)	Saturated Fat (gm)	Choles-terol (mg)
Total	1155.3	165.0	36.9	41.6	6.0	510.3
Per Serving	144.4	20.6	4.6	5.2	0.8	63.8

Orange Coconut Drops

1¼ cups all-purpose flour
1 tsp. baking powder
¼ tsp. baking soda
¼ tsp. salt
⅓ cup diet margarine
⅓ cup flaked coconut

Juice of one
orange
2 tsp. grated fresh
orange peel
1 tsp. vanilla extract
1 egg, beaten

Combine the flour with the baking powder, soda and
salt. Cut in the diet margarine. Stir in the remaining ingredients. Drop by teaspoon 2 inches apart on nonstick cookie sheets. Bake in a preheated 400° oven for
10 to 12 minutes until light golden brown.

(36 servings) Makes 3 dozen

	Calories	Carbo-hydrate (gm)	Protein (gm)	Total Fat (gm)	Saturated Fat (gm)	Choles-terol (mg)
Total	1136.9	140.3	25.1	55.1	20.3	252.0
Per Serving	31.6	3.4	0.7	1.5	0.6	7.0

Cream Puffs

½ cup diet margarine
½ cup water
½ tsp. salt

1 cup sifted all-
purpose flour
4 eggs

Heat the margarine with the water in a medium saucepan over high heat, stirring occasionally, until the margarine melts and the mixture boils. Turn the heat down to low. Add the salt and flour all at once. Stir vigorously until the mixture leaves the sides of the pan in a smooth compact ball. Remove the pan from the heat. Quickly add the eggs — one at a time — beating well after each addition until the mixture is smooth and shiny. Drop the mixture by spoonfuls, 3 inches apart, on an ungreased cookie sheet, shaping each into a mound. Bake the puffs in a preheated 400° oven for 50 minutes. Remove them from the cookie sheet and cool them on a wire rack. To serve, slice the top off each cream puff and fill it with Orange Cream Puff Filling. Then replace the tops. *Makes 18 servings*

	Calories	Carbo-hydrate (gm)	Protein (gm)	Total Fat (gm)	Saturated Fat (gm)	Cholesterol (mg)
Total	1175.0	95.0	37.0	73.0	16.0	1008.0
Per Serving	65.3	5.3	2.1	4.1	0.9	56.0

Orange Cream Puff Filling

6-oz. can frozen
unsweetened
orange juice
concentrate,
defrosted

15 oz. part-skim
ricotta cheese
⅛ tsp. salt

Combine all of the ingredients in a bowl and beat until smooth. Spoon the filling into the Cream Puffs and serve. *Makes 18 servings*

	Calories	Carbo-hydrate (gm)	Protein (gm)	Total Fat (gm)	Saturated Fat (gm)	Cholesterol (mg)
Total	744.0	3.2	84.4	66.0	1.2	32.0
Per Serving	41.3	0.2	4.7	3.7	0.1	1.8

---

gm = grams; mg = milligrams. Nutritional figures are approximate. Figures are based on findings of U.S. Department of Agriculture.

Rum 'n' Honey Fruitcake

1 egg, separated
1⅓ cups graham cracker
   crumbs
3 tbsp. honey
2 tbsp. rum
½ tsp. pumpkin pie spice
½ tsp. bottled orange
   peel (optional)
¾ tsp. baking powder

16-oz. can
   unsweetened
   juice-packed
   fruit cocktail,
   drained
   reserving liquid
½ tsp. salt
3 tbsp. seedless
   raisins
3 tbsp. chopped nuts
   (optional)

Combine the egg yolk, crumbs, honey, rum, pumpkin pie spice, orange peel, and baking powder in a large bowl. Add the juice from the canned fruit cocktail and stir until smooth. Combine the salt and egg white in a separate bowl and whip the egg white until it is stiff. Gently but thoroughly fold the egg white into the batter. Fold in the fruit cocktail, raisins and nuts. Spoon the batter into an 8-inch nonstick cake pan that has been sprayed with vegetable coating. Bake the cake in a preheated 350° oven for 35 to 40 minutes. Allow it to cool thoroughly before slicing.   *Makes 8 servings*

	Calories	Carbo-hydrate (gm)	Protein (gm)	Total Fat (gm)	Saturated Fat (gm)	Choles-terol (mg)
Total	1053.3	175.5	18.1	28.3	2.8	252.0
Per Serving	131.7	21.9	2.3	3.5	0.4	31.5

Orange Cheesecake

2 tbsp. diet margarine
½ cup graham cracker
   crumbs
2 cups 99% fat-free
   cottage cheese
2 tbsp. flour
¼ tsp. butter-flavored
   salt

4 eggs, separated
½ cup evaporated
   skim milk
2 tsp. vanilla
6-oz. can frozen
   orange juice
   concentrate,
   defrosted,
   undiluted

Coat the bottom of a 9-inch spring pan with the diet margarine. Sprinkle the cracker crumbs over the margarine. In a bowl, whip the cottage cheese, flour, and butter-flavored salt until smooth. Add the egg yolks one at a time, mixing well after each addition. Stir in the milk, vanilla, and orange juice. In another bowl, beat the egg whites until stiff, and fold them into the cheese batter. Pour the batter over the crumbs. Bake the cheesecake in a preheated 325° oven for 1 hour. Allow it to cool before removing the rim of the pan. Do not invert the cake.   *Makes 12 servings*

	Calories	Carbo-hydrate (gm)	Protein (gm)	Total Fat (gm)	Saturated Fat (gm)	Choles-terol (mg)
Total	1632.8	156.5	110.7	63.1	23.4	1122.3
Per Serving	136.1	13.0	9.2	5.3	2.0	93.5

Pennsylvania Dutch Cheesecake

Pinch salt
4 egg whites
3 egg yolks
1½ cups 99% fat-free cottage cheese

¼ cup buttermilk
1 tbsp. fresh lemon juice
1½ tsp. vanilla

Beat the salt and the egg whites with an electric mixer until stiff peaks form. Set aside. Put all the remaining ingredients in a blender and blend until smooth and creamy. Pour the cheese mixture into the egg whites. Gently but thoroughly fold together. Spoon the mixture into a 9-inch nonstick square or round cake pan. Bake in a preheated 350° oven for 40 to 50 minutes, until a knife inserted in the center comes out clean. Chill thoroughly. The cake sinks in the center as it cools, making a depression for fresh fruit. Fill with berries or sliced peaches before serving.   *Makes 8 servings*

	Calories	Carbo-hydrate (gm)	Protein (gm)	Total Fat (gm)	Saturated Fat (gm)	Choles-terol (mg)
Total	553.0	16.0	70.1	18.0	7.8	786.4
Per Serving	69.1	2.0	8.8	2.3	1.0	98.3

gm = grams; mg = milligrams. Nutritional figures are approximate. Figures are based on findings of U.S. Department of Agriculture.

Calorie Counter's Whipped Cream

1 cup evaporated skim milk	2 tsp. fresh lemon juice

Pour the evaporated skim milk into a mixing bowl and chill in your freezer until ice crystals begin to form on the milk. Also chill the beaters of your electric mixer. Whip the milk at the high speed of your mixer until it triples in volume. To speed the whipping, add 1 or 2 teaspoons lemon juice for each cup of milk.

Makes 3 cups

	Calories	Carbo-hydrate (gm)	Protein (gm)	Total Fat (gm)	Saturated Fat (gm)	Choles-terol (mg)
Total	352.8	26.6	18.1	20.0	11.0	78.0

Polynesian Fruit Sauce

1 eating orange, peeled and diced ¼ of the orange peel, sliced 16-oz. can unsweetened juice-packed crushed pineapple	2 tbsp. frozen unsweetened orange juice concentrate, defrosted but not diluted 6 tsp. dried shredded coconut (optional)

Combine all of the ingredients except coconut in blender. Cover and process, on and off, until chunky. Use as a topping and sprinkle with coconut.

Makes 6 servings

	Calories	Carbo-hydrate (gm)	Protein (gm)	Total Fat (gm)	Saturated Fat (gm)	Choles-terol (mg)
Total	426.3	89.7	2.7	9.1	7.2	0.0
Per Serving	71.0	15.0	0.5	1.5	1.2	0.0

gm = grams; mg = milligrams. Nutritional figures are approximate. Figures are based on findings of U.S. Department of Agriculture.

Glazed Fresh Fruit for Cheese Pie

2 cups hulled fresh
   strawberries or
   fresh blueberries
1 tbsp. arrowroot or
   cornstarch

1 cup unsweetened
   white or red
   grape juice

If you are using strawberries, leave the small ones whole and slice the large ones in half lengthwise. Arrange the strawberries cut side down on top of a cooled cheese pie. If you are using blueberries, spread them in a single layer over the surface of a cheese pie.

Stir the arrowroot and grape juice together in a saucepan over medium heat until the mixture clears and thickens. Set the pan aside for 10 minutes to cool. Using a spoon, drip the glaze over the fresh fruit. Use only as much as needed to completely coat the fruit. Discard the rest. *Makes 8 servings.*

Hint: If fresh fruit is not available, a 20-ounce can of unsweetened red pitted cherries may be used instead. Use the canned juice in place of the grape juice. If there is not enough juice to make 1 cup, add water. If additional sweetness is desired for either of these glazes, add honey to taste.

	Calories	Carbo-hydrate (gm)	Protein (gm)	Total Fat (gm)	Saturated Fat (gm)	Choles-terol (mg)
Total	300.3	74.2	3.0	2.0	0.0	0.0
Per Serving	37.5	9.3	0.4	0.3	0.0	0.0

Whipped Cheese Topping for Fruit

4 oz. low-calorie
   "imitation" cream
   cheese, or
   Neufchatel cheese,
   softened

¾ cup plain or
   vanilla low-fat
   yogurt

Combine the ingredients and beat until fluffy. Chill before serving. *Makes 1¼ cup (20 servings)*

	Calories	Carbo- hydrate (gm)	Protein (gm)	Total Fat (gm)	Saturated Fat (gm)	Choles- terol (mg)
Total	373.8	13.8	14.0	27.0	17.5	99.9
Per Serving	18.7	0.7	0.7	1.4	0.9	5.0

White Chocolate Cream Topping

15-oz. container part-
skim ricotta cheese
½ cup white crème de
cacao

2 eggs
1 oz. unsweetened
chocolate,
shaved

Combine the ricotta, crème de cacao and eggs in a blender or electric mixer and blend well. Chill and serve sprinkled with the shaved chocolate as a topping on crepes or other desserts.

Makes about 2½ cups (12 servings)

	Calories	Carbo- hydrate (gm)	Protein (gm)	Total Fat (gm)	Saturated Fat (gm)	Choles- terol (mg)
Total	882.0	35.5	98.0	29.0	5.2	536.0
Per Serving	73.5	3.0	8.2	2.4	0.4	44.7

Strawberry Topping

8-oz. pkg. frozen
unsweetened
strawberries,
thawed

2 tbsp. arrowroot or
cornstarch
1 cup undiluted,
unsweetened
red grape juice

Combine all of the ingredients in a saucepan. Cook and stir the mixture over moderate heat until it simmers and thickens. Serve the topping warm or cold.

Makes 12 servings

	Calories	Carbo- hydrate (gm)	Protein (gm)	Total Fat (gm)	Saturated Fat (gm)	Choles- terol (mg)
Total	706.3	181.8	1.9	0.8	0.0	0.0
Per Serving	58.9	15.2	0.2	0.1	0.0	0.0

*gm = grams; mg = milligrams. Nutritional figures are approximate.
Figures are based on findings of U.S. Department of Agriculture.*

Index

Apples
  Apple-Bacon Poultry
    Stuffing, 90
  Apple-Glazed
    Zucchini, 39
  Apple-Raisin Pie,
    117
  Apples au Vin
    Rouge, 102
  Fresh Applesauce,
    104
  Pineapplesauce,
    104
  Raisin-Stuffed
    Baked Apples,
    102
  Tangy Apple
    Coleslaw, 24
Asparagus Stir-Fry, 32

Baked Chicken with
  Mushrooms, 82
Baked Lamb Chops
  with Rice, 67
Baked Tomatoes, 38
Beef, 48–58
  Cider-Spicy Pot
    Roast, 54
  Côte d'Azur Steak
    en Brochette, 55
  Harvest Stew, 58
  Pot Roast Olé, 53
  Rare Roast Beef
    with Teriyaki
    Sauce, 56
  Savory Swiss Steak,
    56
  Slim-but-Saucy Pot
    Roast, 54
  Smothered Baked
    Steak, 57
Bleu Pear Salad, 24
Blueberry Cornmeal
  Muffins, 20

California Carrots with
  Orange Glaze, 35

Calorie Counter's
  Whipped Cream,
    124
Canadian Green
  Beans, 33
Chicken, 79–88
  Baked Chicken with
    Mushrooms, 82
  Chicken Cacciatore,
    83
  Chicken Kiev, 84
  Chicken
    Mediterranean, 82
  Chicken Pizza, 84
  Chicken with
    Vegetables, 87
  Gala Chicken, 88
  Herbed Chicken, 86
  Oven-Fried Chicken,
    85
  Skinnny Fried
    Chicken, 86
Chinese Broccoli with
  Mushrooms, 34
Chinese Pork, 73
Chinese Sweet 'n'
  Sour Lamb, 65
Chopped Steak Suey,
  76
Cider-Spicy Pot Roast,
  54
Coleslaw, 25
  Colorful Coleslaw,
    25
  Tangy Apple
    Coleslaw, 24
Côte d'Azur Steak en
  Brochette, 55
Country Sausage, 22
Cream Puffs, 121
Creamed Broccoli, 34

Easy Cheesy
  Cauliflower, 36
Easy Eggplant
  Parmesan, 37

Fish, see Seafood,
  individual listings
French Turkey Ragout,
  89
Fresh Applesauce, 104
Fresh Mushroom
  Medley, 26
Frosty Fruit Whip, 103
Fruitcake, Rum 'n'
  Honey, 122

Gala Chicken, 88
Garden Salad, 27
Glazed Fresh Fruit for
  Cheese Pie, 125
Gourmet Cauliflower,
  36
Graham Cracker
  Crust, 113

Ham, 69–73
  Ham Patties Aloha,
    71
  Pineapple-Ham Stir
    Fry, 72
Harvest Stew, 58
Herbed Chicken, 86
Herbed Lamb Chops,
  66
High-Protein Egg
  Crepes, 105
High-Protein Waffles,
  21
Hotcakes, 21
Hot Tuna Sandwiches,
  100

Lamb, 64–68
  Baked Lamb Chops
    with Rice, 67
  Chinese Sweet 'n'
    Sour Lamb, 65
  Herbed Lamb
    Chops, 66
  Lamb and
    Artichokes en
    Brochette, 67
  Stir-Fried Lamb with
    Bean Sprouts, 65

Lean Bean Salad, 27
Lemon Zing Dressing, 28
Low-Fat Veal Parmigiana, 62

Meat Loaf for Diet Watchers, 77
Mini-Caloried Marinated Vegetables, 40
Muffins, Blueberry Cornmeal, 20

Orange Cheese Pie, 115
Orange Coconut Drops, 120
Orange Cream Puff Filling, 121
Orange Pumpkin Pie, 120
Oven-Fried Chicken, 85
Oven-Fried Fish Fillets I, 98
Oven-Fried Fish Fillets II, 98

Parsley Potatoes en Casserole, 44
Pear Salad, Bleu, 24
Pennsylvania Dutch Cheesecake, 123
Polynesian Fruit Sauce, 124
Pork, see also Ham, 69–73
Chinese Pork, 73
Country Sausage, 22
Pork Steak Viennese, 71
Savory Sausage, 22
Potatoes
Parsley Potatoes en Casserole, 44
Savory Bacon Potatoes, 44
Stuffed Potatoes, 43

Ragout, French Turkey, 89

Raisin-Stuffed Baked Apples, 102
Rare Roast Beef with Teriyaki Sauce, 56
Rum 'n' Honey Fruitcake, 122

Savory Bacon Potatoes, 44
Savory Swiss Steak, 56
Sea Steak Teriyaki, 97
Seafood, see also individual listings, 91–100
Oven-Fried Fish Fillets I, 98
Oven-Fried Fish Fillets II, 98
Sea Steak Teriyaki, 97
Smothered Fish Steaks, 96
Turkish Baked Sea Steaks, 96
Shell Salad, 45
Shrimp Bisque, 99
Skillet Zucchini Parmesan, 39
Skinny Fried Chicken, 86
Skinny Schnitzel, 63
Skinny Skewered Lamb, 68
Slender Rice, 47
Slim-but-Saucy Pot Roast, 54
Slim-Down Shortcake, 119
Smothered Baked Steak, 57
Smothered Fish Steaks, 96
Snappy Bleu Cheese Dressing, 28
Soup, Italian Pasta, 46
Spiced Fruit Compote, 103
Spring Artichoke Hearts, 32
Stir-Fried Lamb with Bean Sprouts, 65
Stuffed Potatoes, 43

Succulent Burgers, 77
Sugar-Free Strawberries for Shortcake, 119
Summer Squash Bake, 38

Tangy Apple Coleslaw, 24
Tomatoes, Baked, 38
Tuna
Hot Tuna Sandwiches, 100
Tuna with Grapes, 99
Turkey
French Turkey Ragout, 89
Turkey Chili, 78
Turkey Marengo, 89
Turkey Sloppy Joes, 78
Turkish Baked Sea Steaks, 96

Veal, 59–64
Low-Fat Veal Parmigiana, 62
Skinny Schnitzel, 63
Veal Goulash, 60
Veal Piccata, 63
Veal Provencal Petite, 61
Vegetables, see also individual listings, 29–40
Mini-Caloried Marinated Vegetables, 40
Vegetable Medley, 40

Waffles, High-Protein, 21
Whipped Cheese Topping for Fruit, 125
White Chocolate Cream Topping, 126
Wild Rice and Mushrooms, 47